It's another Quality Book from CGP

This book is for anyone studying AQA GCSE Resistant Materials.

Let's face it, D&T is pretty hard-going — you've got a whole load of technical stuff to learn on top of doing your project.

Happily this CGP book helps to take the headache out of all that learning. We've explained all the technical stuff — and drawn plenty of pictures to make the whole thing that bit clearer. Plus we've stuck in some handy hints to help make your project a winner, and some tips on exam technique.

And in true CGP style it's got some daft bits in to try and make the whole experience at least vaguely entertaining for you.

What CGP is all about

Our sole aim here at CGP is to produce the highest quality books — carefully written, immaculately presented and dangerously close to being funny.

Then we work our socks off to get them out to you — at the cheapest possible prices.

Contents

Section Four — Systems

Section Five — Safety and the Environment

Section Six — Industrial Awareness

Published by CGP

Editors:
Katie Braid, Katherine Craig, Ben Fletcher, Sarah Hilton, Adam Moorhouse,
Ali Palin, Hayley Thompson.

Contributors:
Catherine Atsiaris, Ryan Ball, Juliet Gibson, Steven Guinness, Brian Kerrush, John Nichols.

With thanks to Paul Anderson for the content review.
With thanks to Sharon Keeley and Adrian Lee for the proofreading.

With thanks to Laura Stoney for the copyright research.

Photograph on page 8: 'Carlton' by Ettore Sottsass, 1981 — Memphis Milano/Aldo Ballo.

With thanks to BSI for permission to reproduce the Kitemark symbol on pages 12 and 13. Kitemark and the Kitemark symbol are registered trademarks of BSI. For more information visit www.kitemark.com.

Photographs of original oak furniture by Neil Connor on pages 47 and 51 reproduced by kind permission of Anja Connor.

With thanks to Science Photo Library for permission to use the image on page 63.

ISBN: 978 1 84762 353 9

Groovy website: www.cgpbooks.co.uk
Jolly bits of clipart from CorelDRAW®
Printed by Elanders Ltd, Newcastle upon Tyne.

Based on the classic CGP style created by Richard Parsons.

Project Advice

Unlike most subjects, in D&T you actually get to make something useful (well, hopefully).

The Project is Worth 60% of your GCSE

1) Your D&T project is called 'the controlled assessment'.
2) Your teacher will give you as much help as they're allowed to by the exam board, so do ask them... but mostly it's up to you to make a good job of your project.
3) You can dip into this book for a bit of extra help. Section 1 is all about the design process, so if you're not sure where to start, that might be a good place to look.
4) If you're wondering about a particular detail — what type of hinge to use, say — it's probably quickest to look that up in the index and go straight to those pages.

Only Put Relevant Stuff in your Folder

Your teacher will give you plenty of guidance on what needs to go in your folder, but here are some tips:

1) The folder should be no more than 20 sheets of A3. You'll lose marks if you do much more than that.
2) So DON'T waste space on irrelevant stuff, especially at the research stage. For example:

   Say you've analysed some existing TV cupboards, looking at how the doors were attached...

   Don't bore the examiners stupid with detailed descriptions of every TV cupboard hinge within a ten mile radius of your school.

   A brief summary of your research findings is all that's needed — then the really important thing to say is how those findings helped you decide how to attach the doors in your product.

3) DO put in lots of photos. The examiners love this. They want to see photos of:
   - Any models you make (see p.10). Don't just put in photos of the ones that worked. In fact, the ones that didn't quite work are more useful because then you can explain what was wrong and how you fixed it.
   - The intermediate stages of making your final product — part of the way through the assembly process, say — to show how you constructed it.

Here's me with the manufacturer's specification.

4) CHECK that you've used the right technical words and spelled things correctly. And make sure you've explained things clearly — get someone who knows nothing about your project to read it and see if it makes sense.

The Exam is Worth 40%

1) In the exam you'll be tested on everything you've learned during the course — materials, tools, how to design things, how to make things, health and safety, environmental issues...
2) This book can help you learn all that stuff — and has questions for you to check what you know.
3) There's a glossary at the back of the book, in case you need to sort out your thermosetting plastics from your thermoplastics.
4) The exam technique section (pages 70-73) has some worked examples of exam-style questions, and some hints on how to make sure you get top marks.

Controlled Assessment — nope, it's not funny...

When your project is marked, only about a third of the marks are for the final thing you've made and how good it is. Most of the controlled assessment marks depend on the sheer brilliance of your folder.

Design Briefs

If you design and make products that people want to buy, you could become a millionaire.

Market Pull is About What Consumers Want

1) Designers design stuff (and manufacturers make it) to satisfy the wants and needs of consumers — consumer demand. Market pull is when new or improved products are designed as a result of consumer demand.
2) Changing fashions and social attitudes affect the kind of products people want — consumer demand won't always be for the same things or styles.

An example of where market pull has influenced the design of a product is with the car. It was invented as a way of transporting people from A to B, but now consumers expect it to be more of a status symbol, demanding luxury extras like air conditioning, stereos and seat-back TV screens.

Technology Push is About What Manufacturers Can Provide

In industry, research and development departments are always coming up with new technologies, materials and manufacturing techniques. This can drive the design of new products.

1) Manufacturers can use new technology to develop new products, or to improve existing ones.
2) Using new technology might make an existing product cheaper, better at its function or nicer-looking — all things which will make products easier to sell.
3) Computers are a good example. They started off as mechanical 'adding machines' that took up an entire room. Now, thanks to technologies including the microchip, you can buy a sleek, portable laptop that's much faster and more powerful than all those early computers put together.

Designing Starts with the Design Brief

So, someone gets an idea for a new product, either from market pull or technology push. They decide to employ a designer to work on the idea.

1) The person who hires the designer to come up with a design is called the client.
2) The client gives the designer a design brief...
3) The design brief is a starting point for the development of the product. It will probably include:

- what kind of product is needed (and why)
- how the product will be used
- who the product is for (the target market)

DESIGN BRIEF FOR BACKSCRATCHER/TURNIP HOLDER

No currently commercially available backscratcher has an in-built capacity for turnip storage. We want you to design a product to meet this need for those people having itchy backs and modest turnip storage requirements (up to 4 turnips).

In industry, the client supplies the design brief. In the exam, it's the examiner...

Design briefs — to go with your design socks...

So, designers don't just come up with products here, there and everywhere. Products are planned and designed because there's a need for them — whether it's consumer demand or changes in technology.

Design Briefs

Designers take into account what the client wants when they're coming up with ideas. But designers are also influenced by the culture of the society around them — and their designs can influence society too.

Social and Cultural Differences Affect Designing

CULTURE CAN INFLUENCE THE DESIGN OF PRODUCTS...

1) An example of a cultural difference is different ways of eating. Traditionally, Japanese people eat at a low table sitting on the floor.
2) If you were making a table for the Japanese market, it'd have to reflect the culture by having shorter legs than a table for Europeans would.
3) Culture can also affect aesthetic qualities (looks). Some cultures are associated with particular patterns or colours, e.g. green is often associated with Islam — and also with Ireland.

...AND PRODUCTS CAN INFLUENCE SOCIETY

1) Some products can have a powerful influence on how we live. For example:
   - some children sit about playing computer games and watching DVDs indoors (probably while eating crisps) instead of going outside to muck about and get some exercise.
   - affordable cars mean that lots of people drive to big shopping centres, which can put small, local shops out of business.
2) Some products could offend people — products with slogans on, say.
3) Designers have a responsibility to think about the impact of their designs on the society they live in.

The rest of this section describes a typical design process — the sort of thing you'll do for your project and for the design question in the exam.

It's pretty similar to what happens in industry every day.

Practice Questions

1) a) What is meant by market pull?
   b) Give one example of a product that's been introduced because of technology push.
2) a) What information does a design brief include?
   b) In industry, who writes the design brief?
3) In some cultures, people like to eat together in large family groups. Explain how you'd take this into account if you were designing a dining table.
4) a) Give two examples of products that could change people's lifestyles. In each case, describe what the change might be.
   b) Give an example of a design that might offend people and explain why this is offensive.

Product Analysis

Once you've got your design brief, you can start doing some research. It's a good idea to analyse existing products first. This can give you ideas to use in your own designs.

There's Lots to Consider When Analysing a Product

FUNCTION:

Function is what the product is intended to do — its job.
Disassembling (taking apart) a product can help you find out how it works.
Make careful notes as you disassemble something, and record what component parts have been used and how it's structured, using sketches or photos.

FORM:

This is the shape and look of the thing, e.g. colour, texture and decoration.
A product could be old-fashioned or modern-looking. It could have flowing curves or it might be very angular with lots of corners. This is also known as aesthetics.

ERGONOMICS:

Ergonomics is about how easy and comfortable the product is to use. Products need to be designed so that their size and proportions fit the user's needs. For example, a hand-held product needs to fit well in the hand and buttons need to be easily reachable. Designers use body measurement data (anthropometrics) to make sure the product is the right size and shape.

COMPETITION AND COST:

You need to consider value for money. For example, if you're looking at a hairdryer, find out whether it's cheaper or more expensive than similar hairdryers.
You'll also need to look at how it performs compared to these other hairdryers.

SUSTAINABILITY:

Does making or using the product harm the environment? For example, cars emit carbon dioxide (which causes global warming) and various other pollutants. (There's more about sustainability on the next page.)

MATERIALS:

Product analysis should include looking at what materials have been used, and why those materials were chosen.

MANUFACTURE:

Consider all the processes that have been used to make the product. This includes things like which techniques were used to shape the various parts. Don't forget to check if any parts have been assembled separately and plonked into the product later — the term for that is sub-assembly.

Analysing products — an excuse to play with things all day...

You probably think this seems a lot to think about before starting on the design of a product. But it's all worth doing. There's no point coming up with a new product if it's no better than an old one...

Product Analysis

Which Materials are Used Matters

When you're analysing products, think about the environmental impact of the materials used.

1) Some materials are toxic, e.g. some paints and varnishes.
2) Many materials are made from finite resources. For example, there's only a limited amount of metal ores in the Earth's crust. Most plastics are made from crude oil, which will eventually run out.
3) It's better to use sustainable materials, e.g. wood. Softwoods (which can be regrown in a person's lifetime) are a better choice than hardwoods (which take a long time to grow).
4) Products that use recycled materials are also more environmentally friendly.

5) Many products are thrown away — it's good if these products are made from biodegradable materials (materials that will rot away naturally) or recyclable materials. For example, waste wood is biodegradable and can also be recycled into manufactured boards (see page 47).

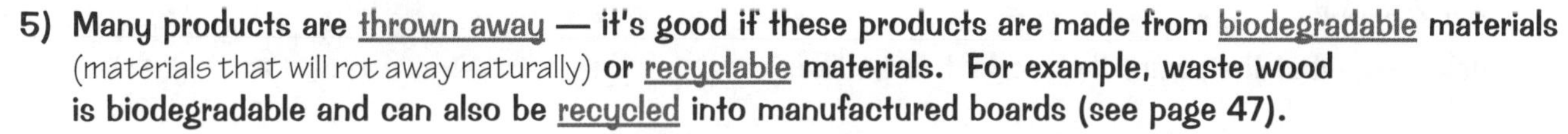

Processes Have Social and Environmental Impacts Too

You should also think about the processes used to make products:

1) Does the manufacturing process cause pollution? For example, how much waste material will be produced and how will it be disposed of?
2) Does the process use a lot of energy? If manufacturers wanted to be extremely responsible, they'd try to use renewable energy sources like wind power or hydroelectricity.
3) Was the product made under good working conditions? For example, does the manufacturer pay workers fairly, give them protective clothing, etc.

Practice Questions

1) Why is it a good idea to analyse existing products?
2) a) What does disassembly mean?
   b) Why is disassembling a product useful?
3) Susanna is analysing the ergonomics of a coffee grinder.
   a) What is meant by ergonomics?
   b) Suggest one part of the coffee grinder that Susanna should consider in detail.
   c) What should she check about this part?

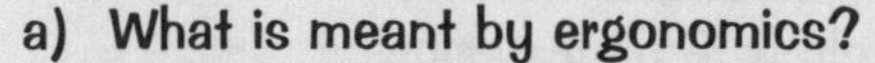

4) Gilbert is analysing a child's toy. He finds that some of the parts are made from plastics, some are metal and some are made from wood.
   a) Which of the materials in the toy are made from finite resources?
   b) Gilbert wants to find out what type of varnish has been used for the wooden parts of the toy. Why is the type of varnish important?
5) Jonathan is selecting a manufacturing process for the chair he has designed. He wants to be environmentally responsible. Suggest two things that he should consider.

Research and Design Specification

There's no point making a product when you don't know that people will actually want it. Though surely everyone will want to buy your multipurpose backscratcher... This is where market research comes in.

Research Your Target Market...

1) The point of doing market research is to:
   - find out what people like or dislike about similar existing products.
   - check that people will actually want your product.
2) Even the best products won't be everyone's cup of tea — some people will like them and some won't.
3) You need to work out which people are most likely to buy your product (the design brief should help) — these people are your target market.
4) Ask them what they want the product to be like.

Designers also get anthropometric data (see page 4) from the target market, and also research the costs of different materials and processes.

...By Giving Them Questionnaires

Questionnaires are just forms for people to fill in. All you have to do is write sensible questions.

There are three basic types of questions:

1) Closed Questions — these have a limited number of possible answers.
   E.g. do you collect turnips?
   Analysing the results is easy for this kind of question.
2) Open Questions — these have no set answer.
   E.g. Why do you collect vegetables?
   They give people a chance to provide details and opinions.
   This type of questioning is more time-consuming and it's harder to draw conclusions from the results. But you could gain more detailed information.
3) Multiple choice questions — these give a choice of answers.
   Sometimes the person answering can pick more than one.

Q4. Which of these vegetables do you collect?
Carrots ☑ Turnips ☐ Potatoes ☐ Onions ☑

Use Your Research to Draw Conclusions

Once you've done some product analysis and market research, you should have loads of information. Now you have to use the information to help with your design.

1) Summarise what you've found out — pick out the most important and useful findings.
   E.g. carrots are just as popular as turnips.
2) Explain what impact each finding will have on your designs.
   E.g. my design should be able to hold carrots as well as turnips.

Draw some conclusions — get your pencil out...

So it's not just playing with existing products — you've got to do some market research too. It's all useful though. Once you've come to some conclusions you can put together your design specification.

Research and Design Specification

The Design Specification is a List of Conditions to Meet

1) The design specification gives certain conditions that the product must meet. These conditions should take account of your research findings.

E.g. if you know that your target market would never buy a backscratcher that costs more than £100, your design specification might include the statement, "Must cost £100 or less."

2) It's best to write a specification as bullet points rather than a paragraph of explanations. Include points to describe some or all of the following:

1. How it should look
2. How it will be used
3. Materials, equipment and production method
4. Size
5. Safety points to consider
6. Price range

Example:

- The backscratcher/turnip holder should weigh 300 g or less.
- It should be multicoloured.
- The minimum length will be 400 mm.
- It should be easy to grip but not feel rough.

EXAM TIP
A good design specification could be worth 6 marks in the exam.

The Specification Guides the Design of the Product

1) The design specification is really important — you refer back to it throughout the project.
2) It acts as a guide to make sure that the product will do what you want it to.
3) You also need it when you come to evaluate your final product.
4) So, it's important that it's clear and detailed — the better it is, the more likely your product will be high quality.

Practice Questions

1) What's the point of doing market research?
2) a) What is meant by a target market?
   b) Ryan is designing a cot for newborn babies. Who are his target market?

3) Juan is designing an egg cup. He wants to send a questionnaire to people in his target market. Suggest:
   a) two closed questions Juan could ask
   b) two open questions he could ask
   c) a multiple choice question he could ask
4) a) What is a design specification?
   b) List some points that the design specification for an egg cup might include.
   c) Write a design specification for a combined egg cup/toast rack.

Generating Proposals

When you're coming up with ideas for products, try to be as adventurous and creative as possible.

There are a Few Tricks That Can Help You Get Started

1) Create a mood board — a load of different images, words, materials, colours...
2) Brainstorm — think up key words, questions and initial thoughts relating to your product. Start off by just writing whatever ideas come into your head and analyse them later.
3) Work from an existing product — but change some of its features or production methods so that it fits in with your specification.

Examiners love it if your ideas include different materials and processes — for example, one idea with hardwood and one with acrylic, some parts made by vacuum forming and other parts made by line bending.

Be Inspired by Successful Designers...

You can look at the work of successful designers to help inspire your own designs.

1) For example, Ettore Sottsass was part of the 'Memphis' design movement of the 1980s. He came up with this design for a bookshelf.

PHOTO: ALDO BALLO

2) You could use a similar style for a totally different product — a clock, say.
3) BUT you mustn't just copy other people's work. Designers protect their designs legally by registering or patenting them. This prevents them being used without permission or payment.

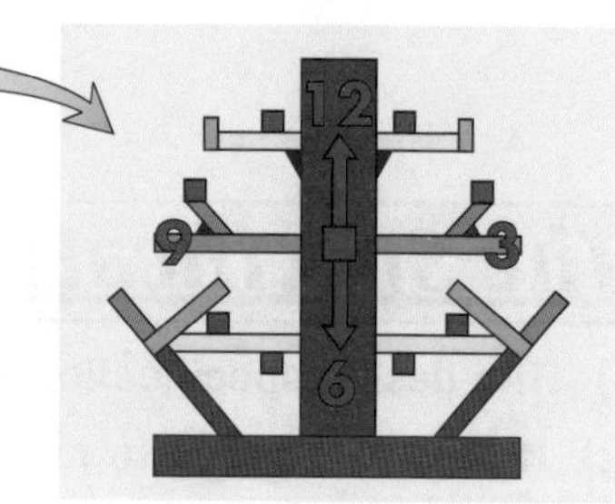

...or Nature...

Nature can be a design inspiration for the structure, function or aesthetics (look) of a product.

Structure

The massive domes at the Eden Project are a very strong, lightweight structure, just like a honeycomb.

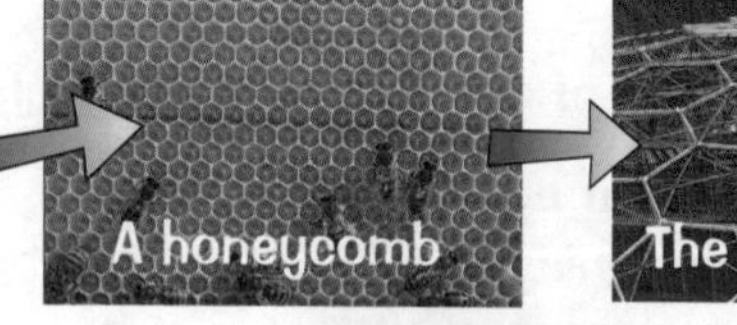

Function

Cats' eyes for roads were invented in the 1930s by Percy Shaw. He was inspired by the way cats' eyes reflect light in the dark.

Aesthetics

A good technique is the close-up effect. This is where you look at just a small section of an image. For example, you could design some jewellery based on a close-up of part of a flower.

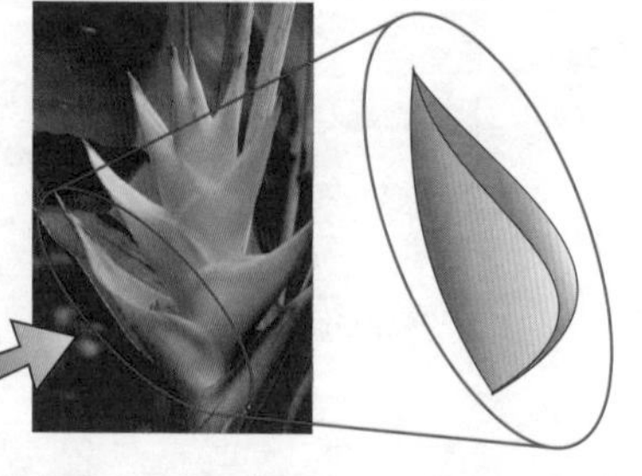

I bet your mood is bored at the moment...

One way of sucking up to your D&T teacher is to say that he/she is your inspiration and then steal their designs. It's probably not a good idea though, so perhaps stick to the world-famous designers...

Generating Proposals

... or Patterns

1) Patterns using grids and repeating shapes are often used in product design.
2) Many products, especially packaging, are based on simple geometric shapes such as squares, rectangles, circles and triangles.

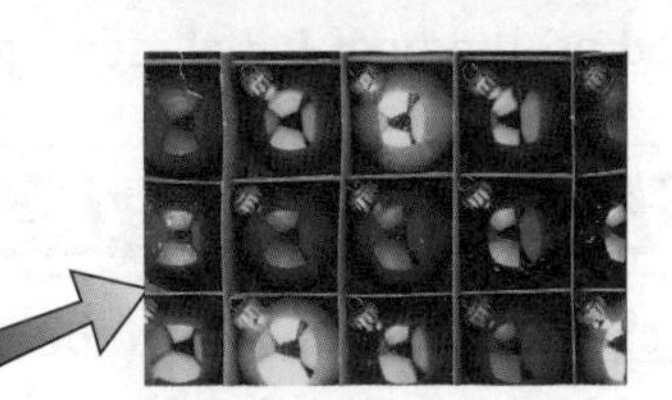

This packaging uses repeated squares.

Another way of generating ideas is to work in a team — this is how it's often done in industry. Different people have different strengths and ideas, and they can inspire each other.

Don't Just Go With the First Thing You Think Of

You need to produce a wide range of different design ideas.

1) Annotate (add notes to) each idea to explain it fully.

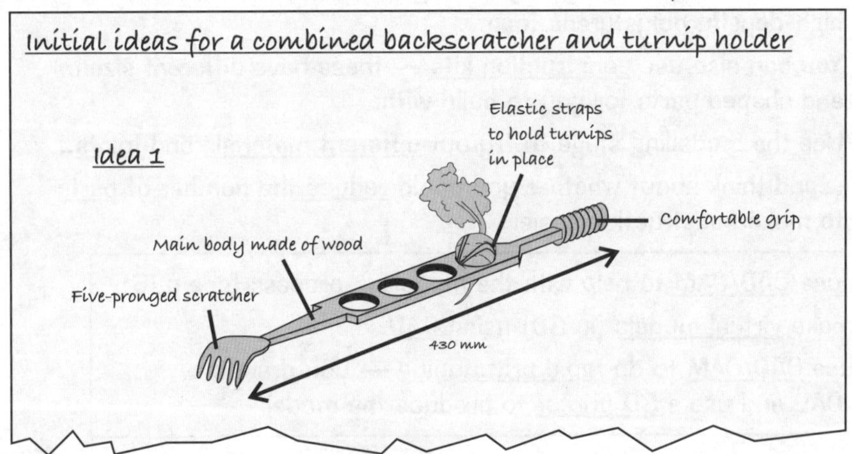

EXAM TIP
Your initial ideas should be sketched freehand in pencil fairly quickly.

2) Once you've got a few possible designs, you need to check that each one matches your specification — any that don't won't be suitable.
3) Also, check that you could actually make the designs. Creativity is a splendid thing... ...but total impracticality isn't.
4) Finally, choose one of your suitable designs to develop further.

Practice Questions

1) Outline three ways of coming up with new ideas for a product.

2) Draw a 'brainstorm' of initial design ideas for a ceiling lamp.

3) Ash is trying to design a basin for his friend's new bathroom. Here is the design specification:
   - a modern look
   - no sharp edges
   - less than 50 cm long by 30 cm wide
   - must include holes for taps
   - easy to clean
   - at least 20 cm deep

   a) Suggest something in nature that Ash could use as an inspiration.
   b) Make an annotated sketch of a design inspired by your suggestion.
   c) Use whatever method you like to come up with two more initial ideas, and sketch and annotate these designs too.

Development

Once you've decided on the best initial idea, you can begin to develop it. Exciting times.

Detailed Sketches Help You Work Out the Finer Points

1) Your initial sketches will probably have been rough, freehand pencil drawings.
2) Trying out some more detailed drawings is the next stage.
3) It helps you to see what will actually work in practice and it might help you decide on details you hadn't thought about before, e.g. the sizes or positions of components or how parts should be constructed and fitted together.

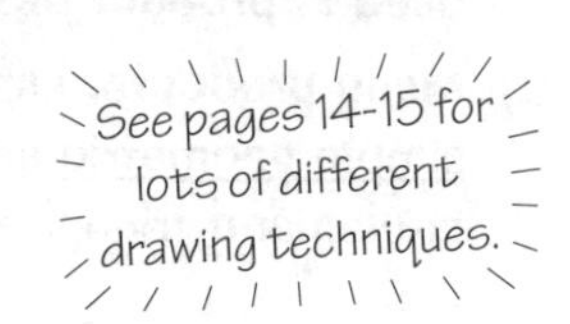

Not that kind of model...

Use Modelling to Improve Your Design

1) Modelling is just making practice versions of your design, or parts of your design. It's a good way to spot (and solve) problems.
2) You can make models using materials that are easy and quick to work with, e.g. cardboard, jellutong (an easily workable wood) or high-density polystyrene foam.
3) You can also use construction kits — these have different sized and shaped parts for you to build with.
4) Use the modelling stage to try out different materials and joints...
5) ...and think about whether you could reduce the number of parts to make construction easier.

You can also use CAD/CAM to help with the modelling process (see p.15).

- You can make virtual models (in 3D) using CAD.
- You can use CAD/CAM to do rapid prototyping — you draw the design in CAD and use a 3D printer to produce the model.

Test and Evaluate Each Model

1) After you've made the first model, do some tests to check that it's how it should be.
2) You'll probably find there are some things that don't work out quite how you'd hoped:

The cupboard looked great
but the doors just couldn't be opened.

3) Write down what the problem is, and suggest how to fix it, e.g. use a different type of hinge.
4) Record how the design develops — take photos of your models.
5) You should also evaluate each model against the design specification. Take each point on the specification and see if your model is up to scratch.
6) You might end up having to modify your specification after you've evaluated your models.

Modelling — take your product down the catwalk...

If you find out that something just can't work or is going to be too expensive, it's OK to change your design — as long as you explain why you've changed it. That's the whole point of testing and evaluation.

Development

Keep Going Until You Get it Just Right

You might find that you end up changing something, then trying it out, then making another change, and so on. That's just the way it goes sometimes.

Here's a summary of the process:

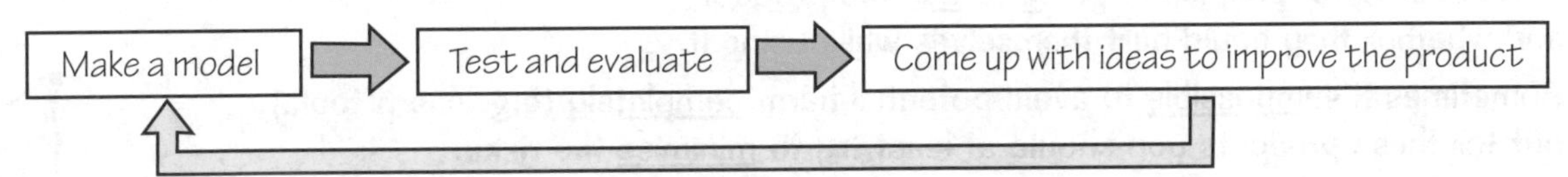
Make a model
Test and evaluate
Come up with ideas to improve the product

Consult Other People About Your Design

1) Find out people's opinions about your various models. (You can do this using market research techniques — see p.6.) This will help you refine your ideas so you can arrive at the best solution.
2) Relevant market research questions might include:
   - Do you find the product comfortable?
   - Is it easy to use?
   - Are you unsure about any of the features? If so, which ones and why?
   - Is it the right size?
   - How much would you be willing to pay?

So would you consider buying one?

For your project, you might also do questionnaires as part of the evaluation of your final product.

3) In industry, you'd also get the client to test the model (to see if it did what they wanted, and if they liked it). You'd also consult some potential manufacturers — to see if they could make it.

Now You Should Know Exactly What You're Making

Once you've finished developing your ideas and have a final design, you should have worked out:

1) The best materials, tools and other equipment to use (and their availability). This might include standard components (see pages 50-51).
2) The approximate manufacturing time needed to make each item.
3) How much it should cost to manufacture each item.
4) The assembly process — this is important when it comes to planning production (see page 17).

Practice Questions

1) Nadia is developing her design by producing more detailed sketches. How will this help her?
2) Explain how CAD/CAM can help at the development stage of designing.
3) Laura wants to make a model of her design for a clock. Suggest some materials she could use for the model.
4) Sasha has finished developing her product — a garden chair. Suggest three market research questions she could ask people when evaluating her final prototype.

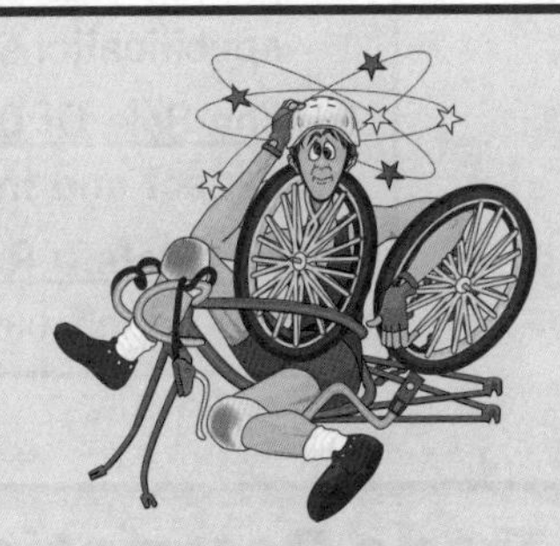

Bob decided that his liquorice-based bicycle frame needed further development.

Designing Safe Products

Safety is really important for the consumer — people don't want to dice with death each time they boil the kettle or turn on the TV. (Understandable, I suppose.)

Products Must be Safe to Use

1) Think about how people are going to use the product and whether they could hurt themselves while using it.
2) Sometimes it's impossible to avoid potential harm completely (e.g. sharp tools), but for these products you should at least try to minimise the risks.

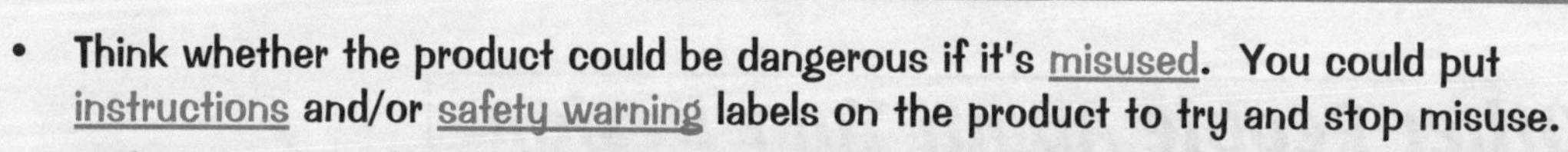

- Think whether the product could be dangerous if it's misused. You could put instructions and/or safety warning labels on the product to try and stop misuse.
- Make sure your design is ergonomic and won't cause long-term health impacts. For example, a chair with a badly designed backrest could cause awful backache after long-term use.
- Products shouldn't have unnecessary sharp corners or edges for people to cut themselves on.
- Toys often end up in children's mouths, so don't finish the surface with a toxic paint or varnish. Check this out at the research stage and choose a non-toxic range of surface treatments.
- Small components must be firmly attached so that a child can't pull them off — this would be a choking hazard. They must be safely attached too — not using sharp metal spikes.
- Use standard components (see p.50-51) wherever you can, because these have already been rigorously tested by their manufacturer — this helps make sure that safety standards are met.

There are Standards for Safety and Quality...

For many products, there are safety and quality standards set by the British Standards Institution (BSI). The BSI independently test products, and if they meet the relevant standards they're awarded the Kitemark — manufacturers can put this on their label (many plastic products have it moulded on).

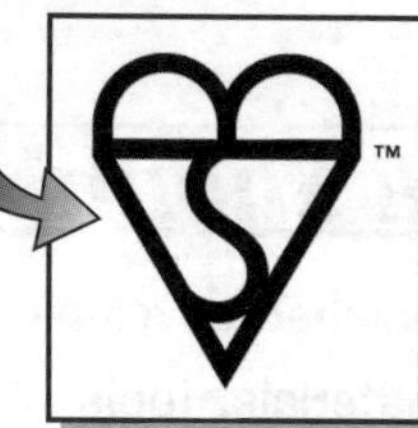

...And Laws Too

Manufacturers who produce unsafe or unreliable products are probably breaking one of these laws:

1) The Trade Descriptions Acts ensure that any claims made about a product (e.g. that it is hard-wearing, long-lasting, waterproof) must be true.
2) The Consumer Safety Act covers fire regulations and specifications for clothing, toys, electrical goods, etc.
3) The Sale Of Goods Act ensures that products perform as you would expect and that goods last a reasonable length of time.
4) Fire Safety Regulations cover upholstered furniture and cushions, etc. to ensure that they don't catch fire easily and don't give off really toxic fumes when they burn.

Trade Descriptions — it's all an act...

As if you didn't already have enough to think about... When you're designing a product, you also need to keep the safety of the consumer in mind, particularly if the product is aimed at a young child.

Designing Safe Products

Labelling Gives Important Information...

1) As well as the BSI, other institutions and associations also award safety or quality marks to products that meet their standards. For example, the British Electrotechnical Approvals Board (BEAB) awards electrical safety marks that can be shown on labels.
2) Certain types of product must also meet EU standards for safety, shown by the 'CE' mark, before they can be sold in most European countries.
3) As well as showing that a product has met safety standards, labels can give other useful information:

"store out of direct sunlight"

"clean with mild detergent only"

↑ THIS WAY UP ↑

...Including Safety Warnings

You might think this is a nice, harmless novelty sticky-tape holder...

But just look at its safety label. Not looking so cute now.

THIS IS NOT A TOY, CONTENTS NOT FIT FOR CONSUMPTION.
IF CONTACT WITH OIL OCCURS, WASH WITH SOAP & WATER.
DO NOT LEAVE IN DIRECT SUNLIGHT AS LIQUID MAY DISCOLOUR.
NOT SUITABLE FOR CHILDREN UNDER 6 YEARS.
CONTAINS SMALL PARTS WHICH COULD REPRESENT A CHOKING HAZARD

OK, so you probably weren't going to eat it anyway, but there is some useful advice too.

Practice Questions

1) Name a product where it's impossible to completely prevent potential harm. Explain why.
2) Give two examples of how to minimise risk when designing toys.

3) Why is it a good idea to use standard components wherever possible?
4) a) What is the symbol on the left?
   b) What does the symbol show?

5) Katie is designing a bed. She is assessing whether her product will break any laws. Which laws cover the following things?
   a) Whether the bed will last a long time.
   b) Whether the mattress will give off toxic fumes if it catches fire.
6) What does the 'CE' mark show?
7) Ben has designed a table lamp. It has a wooden base and brass shade. Suggest two instructions or warnings he might put on the label.

Drawing Techniques

Perspective Drawing Uses Vanishing Points

1) Perspective drawing tries to show what something actually looks like — smaller in the distance, larger close up. It does this by using lines that appear to meet at points called vanishing points.
2) These points are in the distance on the horizon line.

One-Point Perspective — for drawing objects head on.

1) Mark one vanishing point.
2) Draw the front view of the object head on.
3) Then draw lines to the vanishing point.

vanishing point

EXAM TIP
Practise the techniques on these two pages — you'll have to use them for the design question in the exam.

Two-Point Perspective — for drawing objects at an angle.

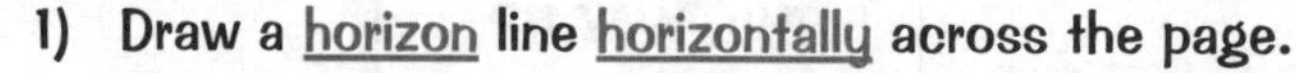

1) Draw a horizon line horizontally across the page.
2) Mark two vanishing points near the ends of the horizon line.
3) Draw the object by starting with the front, vertical edge and then projecting lines to the vanishing points.
4) Remember that vertical lines remain vertical and all horizontal lines go to the vanishing points.

Isometric Drawing Shows Objects at 30°

1) Isometric drawing can be used to show a 3D picture of an object.
2) It doesn't show perspective (things don't get smaller in the distance), but it's easier to get dimensions right than in perspective drawing.
3) There are three main rules when drawing in isometric:

- Draw vertical edges on the object as vertical lines.
- Draw horizontal edges on the object at 30°.
- Check that parallel edges on the object appear as parallel lines on your drawing.

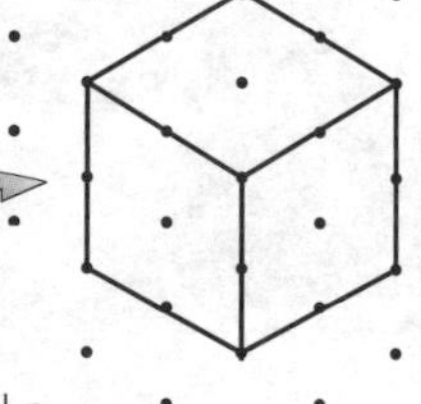

This drawing's been done on isometric grid paper.
You could use plain paper and a 30°/60° set square instead.

Assembly Drawings Show How Things Fit Together

Exploded views and sectional drawings are two types of assembly drawing.

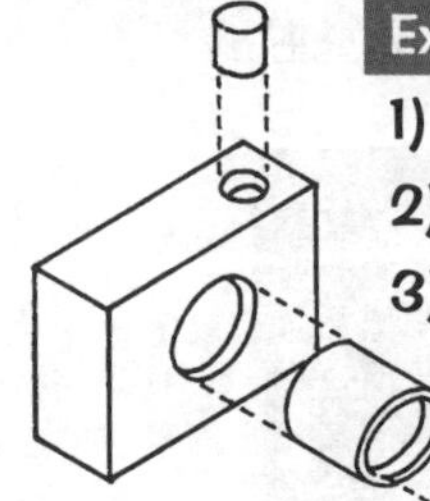

Exploded views

1) You draw the product with each separate part of it moved out as if it's been exploded.
2) Each part of the product is drawn in line with the part it's attached to.
3) Dotted lines show where the part has been exploded from.

Sectional drawings show what the product would look like inside if you cut it in two.

In this diagram the product is imagined to be cut in half through section X,Y.

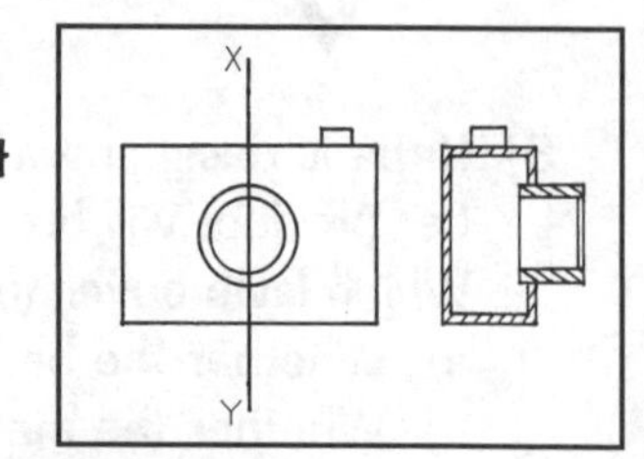

Sir, I lost my work — must be down a vanishing point...

Your drawings will look more realistic if you render them — this means adding shading and/or colour. It's well worth practising because there are marks going for it in both the project and the exam.

Drawing Techniques

CAD is Computer Aided Design

1) CAD (Computer Aided Design) can be very useful when you're developing your ideas.
2) CAD software ranges from 2D drawing programs (e.g. TechSoft 2D Design) to 3D modelling packages (e.g. Pro/DESKTOP® or SolidWorks®).
3) CAD helps designers model and change their designs quickly. It's easy to experiment with alternative colours and forms and you can spot problems before making anything.
4) In 3D programs, you can view the products from all angles.
5) Another advantage is that you can do rapid prototyping (see p.35) of your design using CAD/CAM.

CAD/CAM systems work by using x, y, z coordinates. The CAD software works out the coordinates of each point on your drawing — x is the left/right position, y is forwards/backwards and z is up/down. A CAM machine can follow these coordinates and move the tools to cut out (or build up) your design.

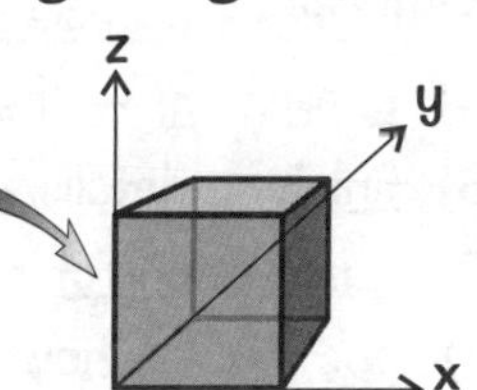

Orthographic Projection Shows 2D Views of a 3D Object

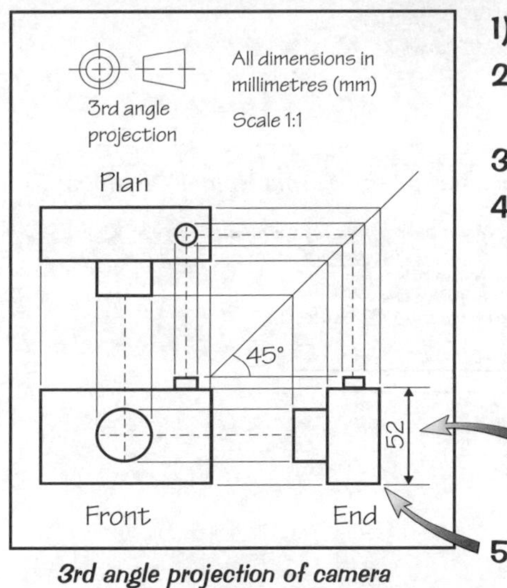

3rd angle projection of camera

1) The symbol for 3rd angle orthographic projection is:
2) The front view, plan view and end view of the product are drawn accurately to scale.
3) Dimensions are always given in millimetres.
4) To avoid confusion, lines and dimensions must conform to the following British Standards recommendations:
   - outlines: thick and continuous
   - projection/construction lines: light and continuous
   - centre lines: alternate short and long dashes, light
   - hidden details: short dashes, light
   - 34 — dimension lines: medium and continuous, with solid arrowheads and the dimension written above the line in the middle (or to the left of the line if it's angled or vertical)
5) There's always a gap between the projection lines and the object.

Practice Questions

1) Draw this desk from the front using one-point perspective.

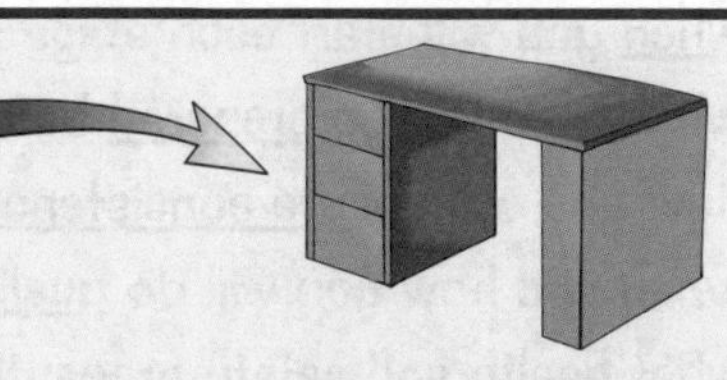

2) Give one advantage and one disadvantage of using isometric drawing rather than perspective drawing.
3) Do an exploded view drawing to show the part of the submarine on the left, including the turrets.

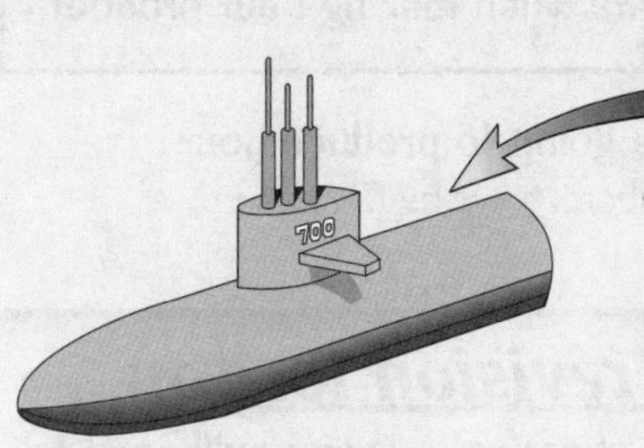

4) Caroline is designing a child's toy. Suggest a software package she might use to draw the toy in 3D.
5) In orthographic projection:
   a) What types of lines should be dashed?
   b) What units must the dimensions be given in?

Planning for Manufacture

In industry, designers usually just design things — they don't make them as well.
So they have to tell the manufacturer exactly what the product is and how to make it.

You Need to Produce a Manufacturer's Specification

A manufacturer's specification can be a series of written statements, or working drawings and sequence diagrams (see next page). It has to explain exactly how to make the product, and should include:

1) clear construction details explaining exactly how to make each part,
2) materials — which materials to use for each part and how much will be needed,
3) sizes — precise measurements of each part in millimetres,
4) tolerances — the maximum and minimum sizes each part should be,
5) finishing details — any special information, such as 'varnish these parts before assembly',
6) quality control instructions — when and how checks should be made.
7) costings — how much each part costs, and details of any other costs involved.

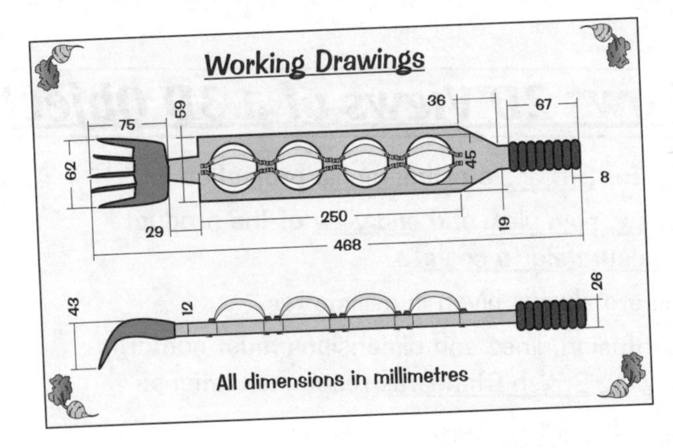

EXAM TIP
Dimensions must be given in millimetres — you'll lose marks otherwise.

Spreadsheets are great for working out costings.

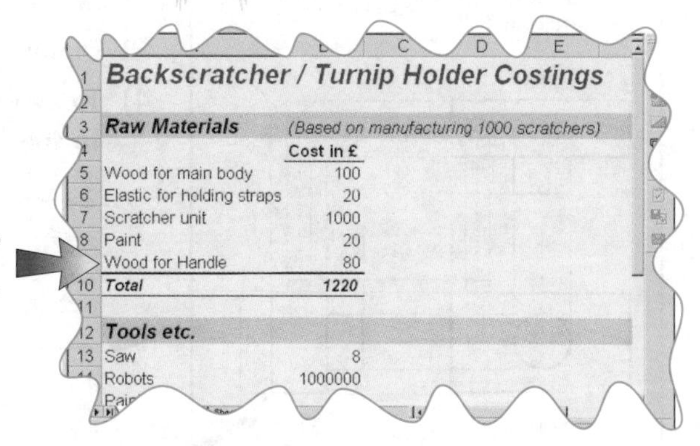

1	Backscratcher / Turnip Holder Costings	
2		
3	Raw Materials	(Based on manufacturing 1000 scratchers)
4		Cost in £
5	Wood for main body	100
6	Elastic for holding straps	20
7	Scratcher unit	1000
8	Paint	20
9	Wood for Handle	80
10	Total	1220
11		
12	Tools etc.	
13	Saw	8
14	Robots	1000000

Plan Each Stage in Detail

Take each stage of the process and plan it in detail. You also need to think about:

1) when you will start each stage and how long it will take.
2) what needs to be prepared before you can start each stage.
3) how you will ensure consistency and quality, e.g. using jigs, formers and measuring tools.
4) when and how you will do quality control checks.
5) what health and safety precautions you will have to take to be safe when making your product.

Remember, your methods would probably change if you were going to produce your design in quantity. (In your project, you should definitely write about how they'd change.)

Working drawings — if only they did your revision for you...

For your project you obviously have to make the product yourself (no cheating). Then you'll need to test it against your specification and similar products available to buy — and write a full evaluation.

Planning for Manufacture

Making a few examples of your product is (relatively) easy. But mass-producing it is a whole different ball game. And it takes a shed-load of careful planning.

(You can of course plan things in a shed, while bouncing a ball against the wall.)

Use Charts to Help You

You need to work out what order to do things in.

1) **Work Order** This can be produced as a table or flow chart. The purpose of a work order is to plan in sequence each task to be carried out. This could include tools and equipment, quality control stages, safety, and so on.

Day	Process	Tools needed
1	Cut main block of wood	Panel saw
	Cut 4 turnip-holder holes	Drill, fret saw
2	Paint main block of wood	Paint, paint brush

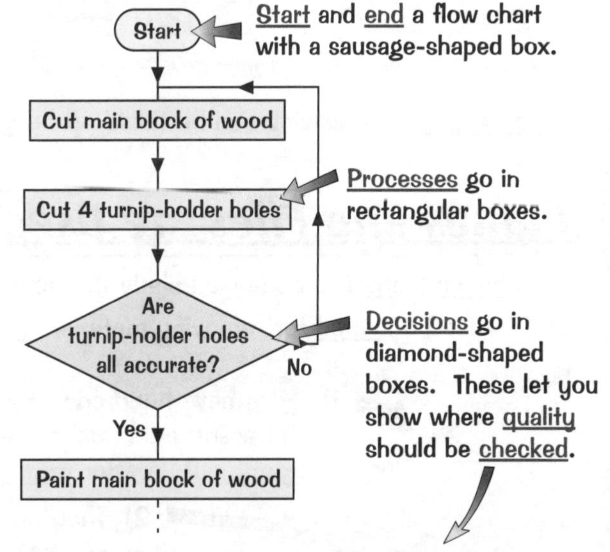

The diamond shaped boxes show where you will stop and see if your product looks and works how it should. If you find it doesn't, go back and make sure it's done properly before you move on.

You also need to work out how long each stage will take, and how these times will fit into the total time you've allowed for production. One way to do this is with a Gantt chart:

2) **Gantt Chart** The tasks are listed down the left-hand side, and the timing is plotted across the top. The coloured squares show how long each task takes, and the order they're done in.

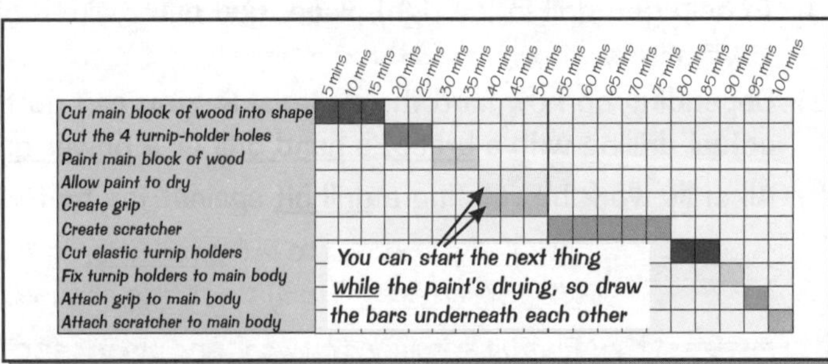

Practice Questions

1) a) What is a manufacturer's specification?
   b) List three things that a manufacturer's specification might include.

2) What are working drawings?

3) On a flow chart, how would you show where quality control should take place?

4) Mike is making a table. He has made a Gantt chart of the process.
   a) Why do some of the bars overlap?
   b) How long does the whole process last?
   c) Which is the longest stage? How long does it last?

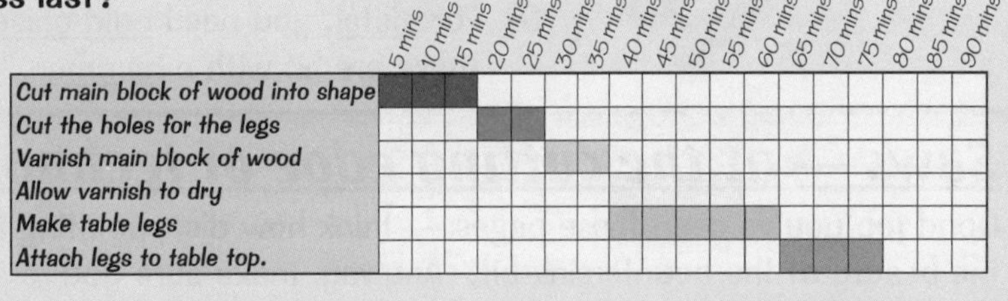

Hand and Power Tools

There are plenty of hand and power tools out there for cutting and shaping materials.

Saws are the Main Cutting Tools

Saws have to be kept sharp, either by sharpening or replacing the blade.

There are different saws for different materials:

Ripsaw — for wood

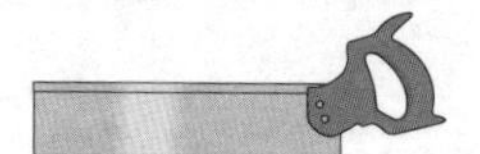
Tenon saw — for wood

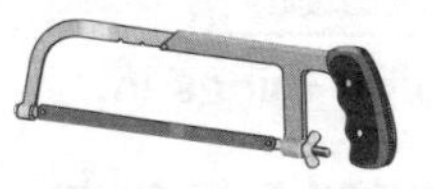
Hacksaw — for metals and plastics

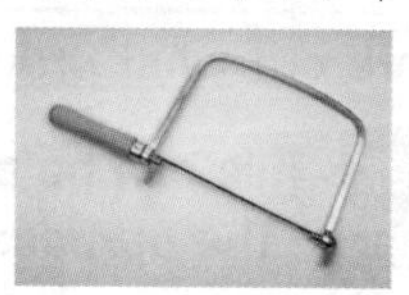
Coping saw — for cutting curves in wood or plastic

Rough edges from sawing can be tidied up by sanding or planing.

Planes and Files are Used for Shaping and Smoothing

1) A bench plane has an angled blade that shaves off thin layers of material.
2) It's used on wood for removing material (shaping).

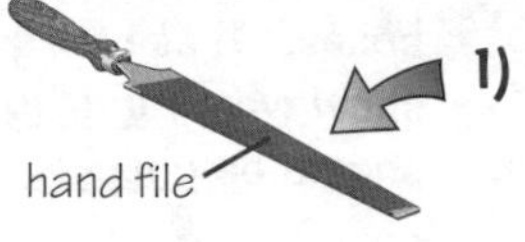

1) Files have hundreds of small teeth to cut away at a material. Different 'cuts' make them suitable for different processes: rough cuts are for removal of material, fine cuts are for finishing (final smoothing).

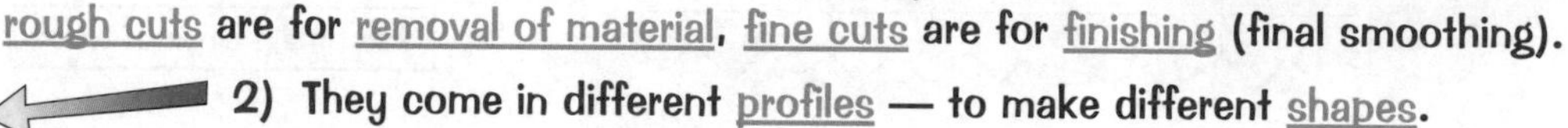

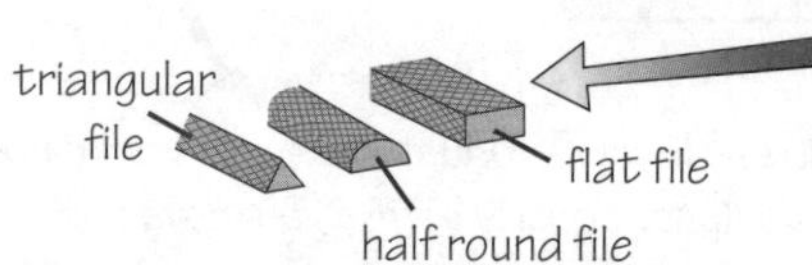

2) They come in different profiles — to make different shapes.
3) Most files are meant for metals and plastics, but there are special ones with very coarse teeth called cabinet rasps for use on wood.

Drills Make Holes (no kidding...)

1) To help you drill in the right place, you can make a pilot hole first using a bradawl.

Bradawls can only be used on wood and plastic. You'd use a centre punch for metal.

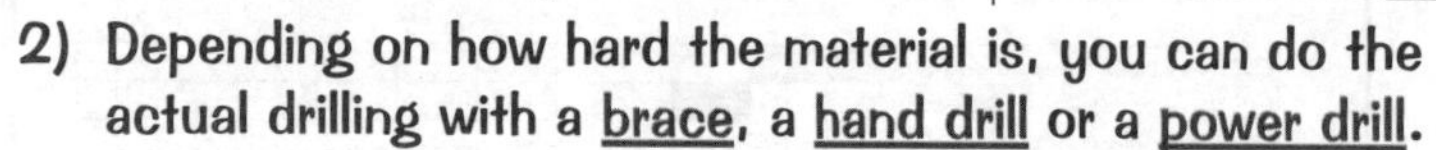

2) Depending on how hard the material is, you can do the actual drilling with a brace, a hand drill or a power drill.
3) All drills work by rotating a drill bit against the material.

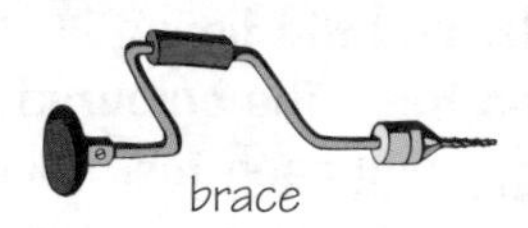
brace

hand drill

Twist bits are used to drill small holes in wood, metal or plastic. High speed steel (HSS) twist bits are used on metals and plastics.

Flat bits are used on wood and plastics to drill large flat-bottomed holes.

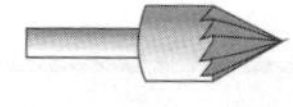
Countersink bits make holes for screw heads to sit in.

Chisels are Used for Shaping

Chisels are used to cut away and shape wood and metal.

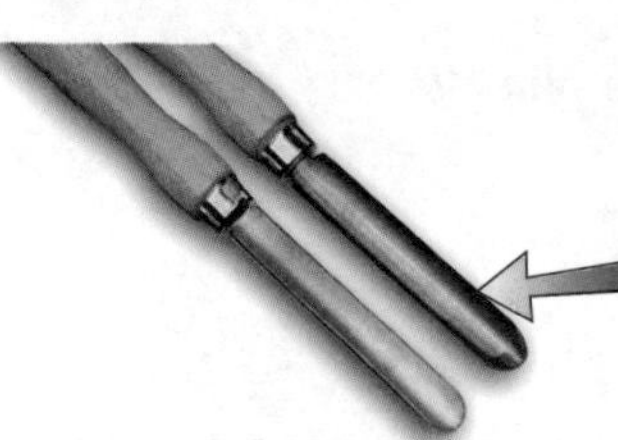

1) Wood chisels come in different profiles for making different shapes. You hit them with a mallet.

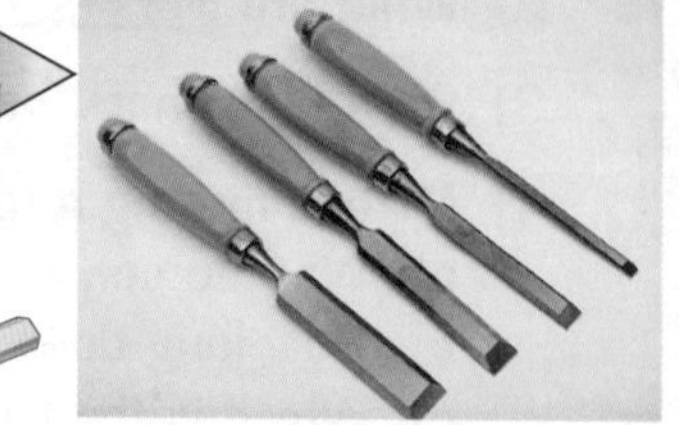

2) Gougers are used for sculpting.
3) For metal, you need cold chisels. These are hit with a hammer.

Saws — at the cutting edge of technology...

Good job you've seen these pages — think how disappointing it would have been never to have known the beauty of the countersink bit. Anyway, make sure you're able to suggest the right tool for the job.

Hand and Power Tools

Power Tools are Hand-held Motorised Tools

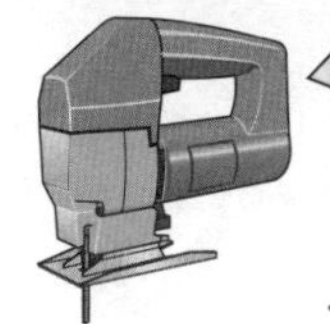

1) A **jigsaw** has interchangeable blades and variable speeds.
2) You can make straight or curved cuts in all materials, but it's quite slow.

1) You can get a hand-held version of the **circular saw** (see page 20).
2) The wood is held stationary and the saw is moved along it, using adjustable fences for guidance.
3) It's good for making straight cuts very quickly in wood.

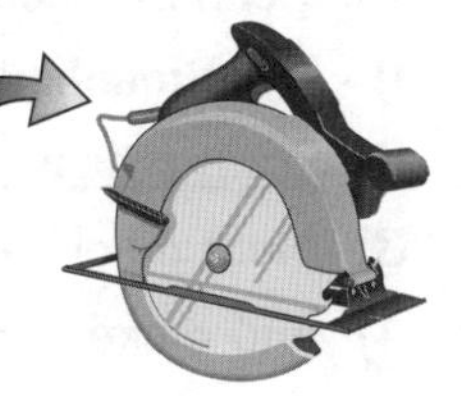

1) A **planer** is used like a bench plane to remove shavings of wood — either to reduce the material to the required size, or for rough shaping.
2) The advantage of a power planer is that it takes much less effort and is much faster — but it's not as accurate as a bench plane.

Accuracy is Really Important

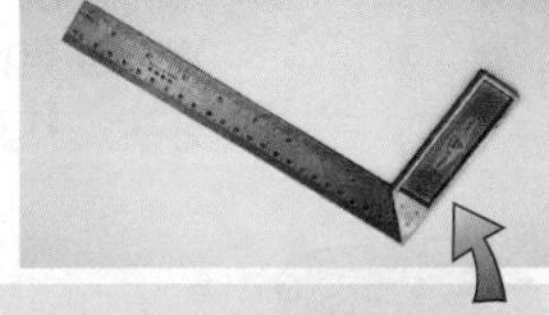

1) You need to mark out carefully before you cut or shape your material.

For example... To mark a right angle from the edge of the material and to check that edges are square, use a try square. Use a centre punch to mark where you want to drill a hole in metal.

2) You can use a template (see page 68) if you're marking out lots of the same shape — this will ensure that each one is the same.
3) You can't mark and cut everything perfectly — no-one's perfect. But it's important to work within the required tolerance (set down in a manufacturer's specification — see page 16). Tolerance is the amount by which the size of parts can differ without affecting the product — it's your room for error.

Say you're cutting some wood to size. It's meant to be 60 mm wide, but the tolerance is ± 2 mm.
You need to check that what you've cut is within the tolerance — 58 mm to 62 mm.
If it's 63 mm, plane off more material to make it right. If it's 56 mm, you'll have to start again ☹.

Practice Questions

1) What type of saw is used for cutting metals?
2) What is a coping saw used for?
3) Phil wants to make a pilot hole before he drills a hole for a screw in a piece of wood. Suggest what tool he could use to make the pilot hole.
4) Name two types of drill bit and say what they're used for.
5) Paul wants to remove some shavings of wood from a table he is making.
   a) Suggest a hand tool and a power tool that he could use to do this.
   b) Give one reason why Paul might choose to use the hand tool.
6) Caroline is making a cupboard.
   a) Name two marking out tools she could use and suggest what she would use them for.
   b) The manufacturer's specification tells Caroline to drill a hole 35 mm from the top of the door, ±3 mm. What is the furthest the hole could be from the top of the door?

Machine Tools

Machine tools do the same jobs as hand-held tools — but a lot faster and more accurately.

Machine Tools are Great if You Use them Safely

These are usually stationary and are often bolted to the workbench or the floor.
They can be used to process large quantities of material accurately and quickly.

1) Most machines used for wood are attached to a dust extractor.
2) Safety glasses should be worn, hair tied back and clothing tucked in — to avoid horrible accidents.
3) Most machine tools have guards to help keep you safe — use them.
4) And make sure you know where the big, red emergency stop button is — just in case.

There are Some Ace Machines for Cutting and Drilling

Whether you have these tools in your D&T workshop or not, you still need to know what they're for.

The circular saw or saw bench has a round blade and is used to cut wood and boards like plywood to size. It makes straight cuts only.

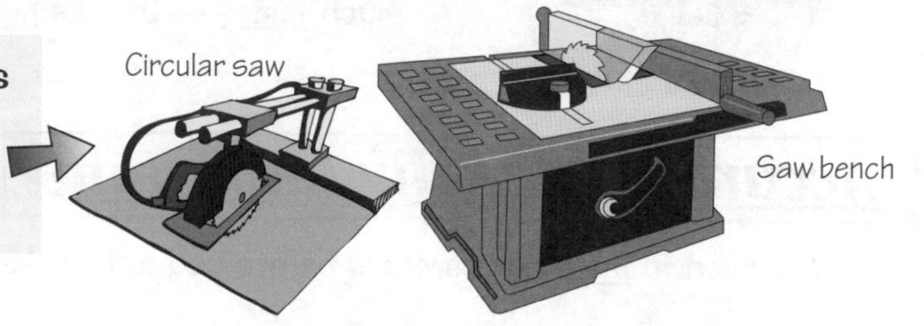

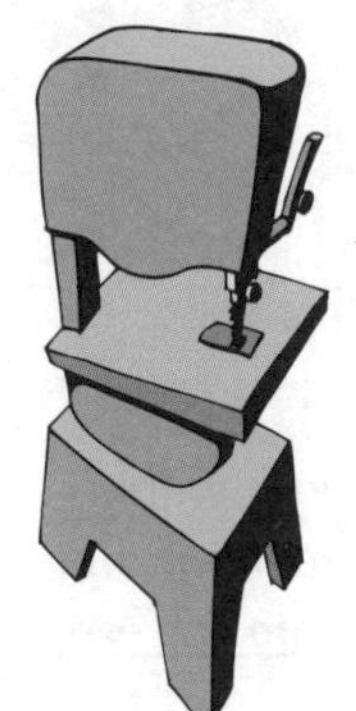

The band saw has a blade in a long flexible loop and is normally used to cut wood, but special blades can be bought for use on plastics and softer metals. The blades come in different widths and can be used for straight or curved cuts.

A planer and thicknesser (either separate or both in a single machine) are used for flattening the surface of pieces of wood and for reducing their thickness to a specified measurement.

A pillar drill or pedestal drill is used to make round holes. They can be used on all kinds of materials, depending on the drill bit used (see page 18).

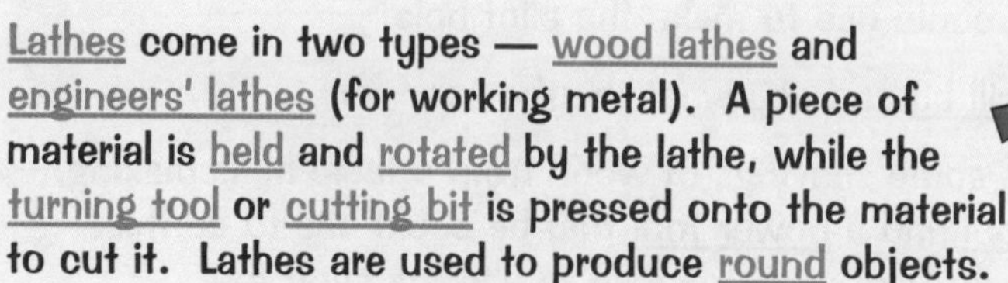
Lathes come in two types — wood lathes and engineers' lathes (for working metal). A piece of material is held and rotated by the lathe, while the turning tool or cutting bit is pressed onto the material to cut it. Lathes are used to produce round objects.

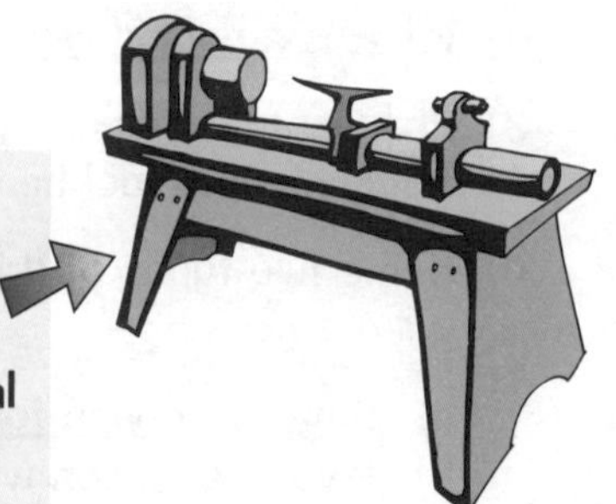

The band saw — the most musical of the machine tools...

Hold your horses. Even if you've used a machine tool to cut some material, you still need to check that the part you've made is within the tolerance. Don't just assume that it'll be accurate — oh no.

Machine Tools

Just Wait Till You See These Sanders and Grinders

Aah... these little beauties...

1) A **sanding disc** spins a disc of abrasive paper which the material's pushed against.
2) It's used for trimming accurately to a line.
3) Different types of abrasive paper are available for use on wood, metal, and plastics.

1) A **bench grinder** contains abrasive wheels of different grades (coarse to smooth).
2) It's used to remove metal for shaping or finishing purposes, as well as for sharpening edged tools such as chisels.

This is a lathe and milling machine in one — clever stuff

1) A **milling machine** is used to remove material one thin layer at a time to produce the required size or shape.
2) It can also be used to make a surface absolutely flat.
3) It can produce a very accurate finish.

If you're producing a batch of something, remember that templates and jigs (page 68) can be useful for making sure all of the parts are the same.

Practice Questions

1) Give two advantages of using machine tools rather than hand or power tools.
2) Give two safety precautions that must be taken when working with machine tools.
3) What would you use a circular saw for?
4) Susan is making a door. She wants to smooth the surface of the wood and cut it down to the right thickness. Suggest two machine tools that she might use to do this.
5) Calum works in a factory making moulds from metal. Suggest what machine tool he could use for removing metal to produce the shape of the mould.
6) Give two uses of a bench grinder.

Forming and Bending

When you're making a product, you often need to change the shape of a material. The way you do this depends on the material you're using.

Sheet Metals Can be Folded

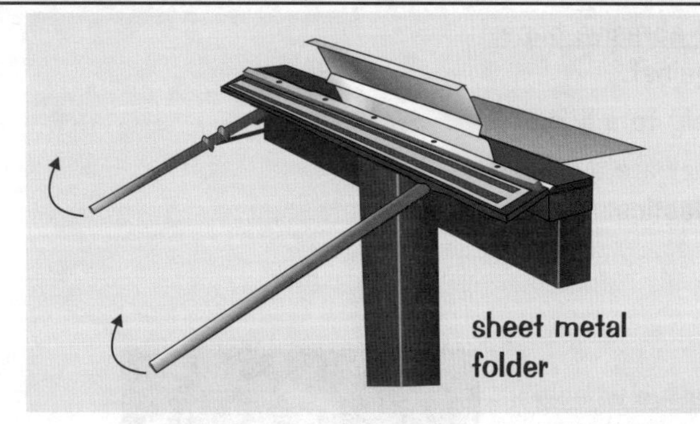

1) You can use a sheet metal folder to shape sheet metals such as aluminium and tin plate.
2) The outline of the product, e.g. a box, is marked out and cut from a flat sheet of metal.
3) You feed the metal in flat, make one fold then move the material through for the next fold.
4) Corners can then be joined using rivets, or by soldering, brazing, etc. — see page 32.

Most Metals Need to be Heated Before Bending

1) Some thin pieces of metal can be bent cold on a jig or former.
2) Thicker or harder metals have to be heated or annealed first (see page 40) and allowed to cool.
3) This makes them soft enough to bend easily, but the annealing process might have to be repeated as bending makes them go hard again — this is known as 'work hardening'.

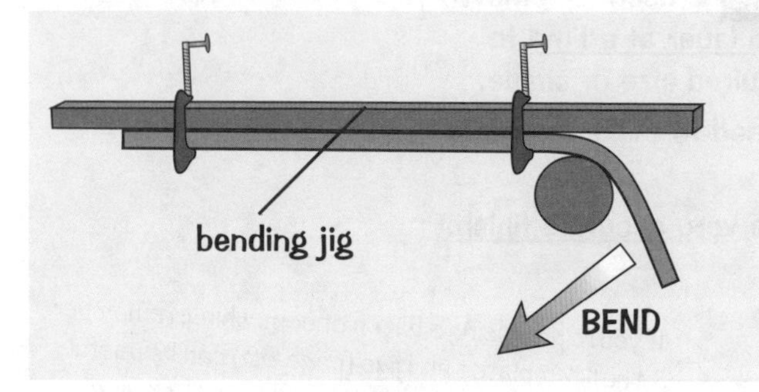

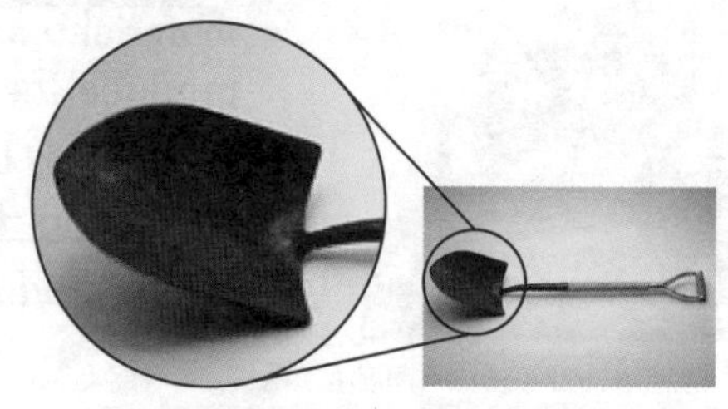

Metal would have been heated and bent to make this shovel.

Iron and Steel are Forged

1) Metal, especially iron and steel, can be heated in a forge.

2) A forge is a fire with air blown into the middle of it to produce a very hot flame.
3) When the metal's hot enough to have softened sufficiently, it's taken out and hammered into shape on an anvil.

You need to bend your brain around this page...

Different materials are bent using different methods. Makes sense really — you wouldn't really want to try forging plastic, for example. You'd just get a gooey puddle that wouldn't be much use for anything.

Forming and Bending

Wood and plastics can be bent and folded too.

Laminating is Gluing Thin Strips of Wood Together

Thin strips of wood (usually 2-6 mm thick)...

...are glued together and held in a jig, which keeps them in the right shape till the glue has dried.

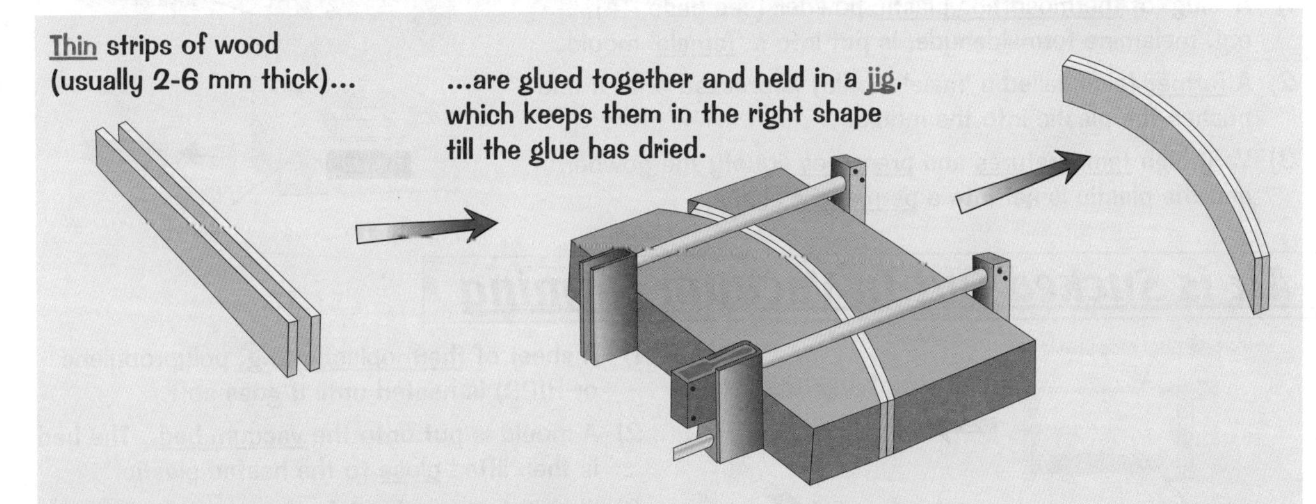

Things that could be made this way include rocking chair runners, chair or table legs and roof beams.

Plastics Can Also be Folded

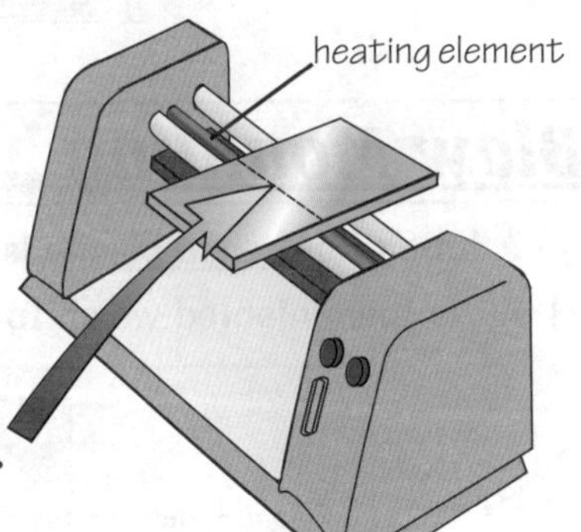
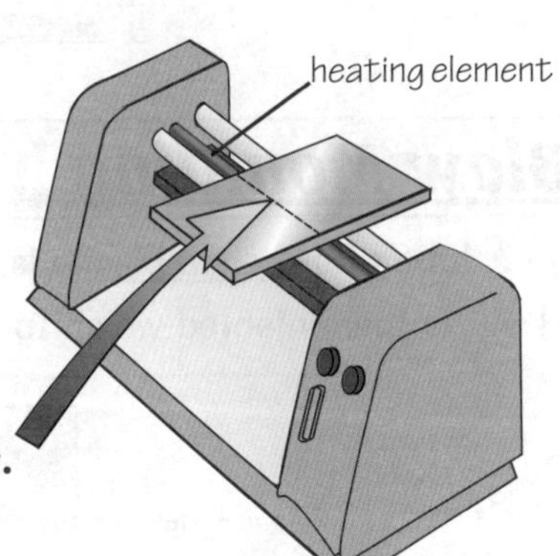

1) Line bending is ideal for use with acrylic sheets, e.g. for making picture frames and pencil holders, etc.
2) It can be done manually or with a line bender or strip heater.
3) You rest the sheet on two bars and the element between them heats the plastic. You just need to position the sheet carefully, so that the line you want to bend along is directly above the element.

Practice Questions

1) What machine could you use to make this metal magazine rack?

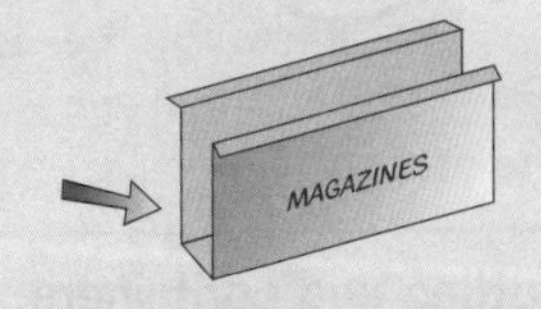

2) Sid wants to bend a thick piece of metal into the shape shown on the right.
   a) What does he need to do before he can bend the metal?
   b) Sketch a diagram to show how he can bend the metal using a bending jig.

3) What is an anvil used for?

4) a) Outline how laminating can be used to make bent wooden items.
   b) Suggest two products or components made by laminating wood.

5) Emma needs to fold a piece of acrylic for the picture frame she is making.
   a) Name a process she could use to fold the acrylic.
   b) Outline what happens during this process.

Casting and Moulding

There are plenty of ways to mould things — pressing, sucking and blowing just for starters.

Press Moulding Shapes Thermosets

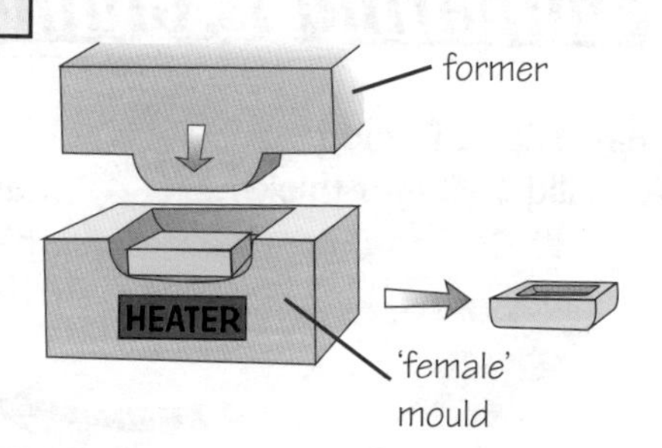

1) A 'slug' of thermosetting plastic powder (see page 44), e.g. melamine formaldehyde, is put into a 'female' mould.
2) A former (also called a 'male' mould) is pressed onto it and pushes the plastic into the mould.
3) Very high temperatures and pressures liquefy the powder, and the plastic is set into a permanent shape.

Air is Sucked Out In Vacuum Forming

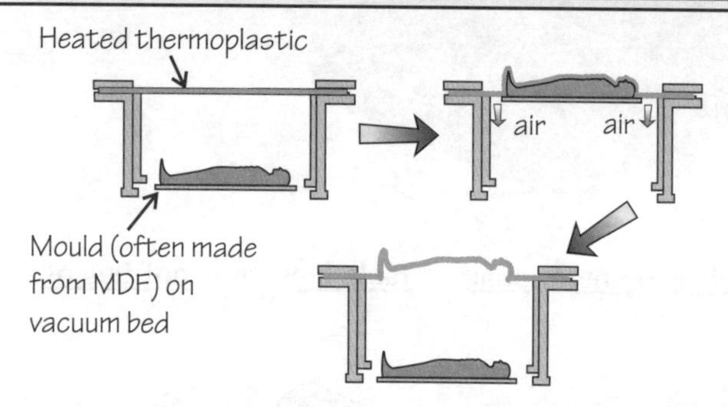

1) A sheet of thermoplastic (e.g. polypropylene or HIPS) is heated until it goes soft.
2) A mould is put onto the vacuum bed. The bed is then lifted close to the heated plastic.
3) The air is sucked out from under the plastic, creating a vacuum. The air pressure from outside the mould then forces the plastic onto the mould.

Blow Moulding... Well... Blows Air In

1) A tube of softened plastic is inserted into a solid mould.
2) Air is then injected which forces the plastic to expand to the shape of the mould:

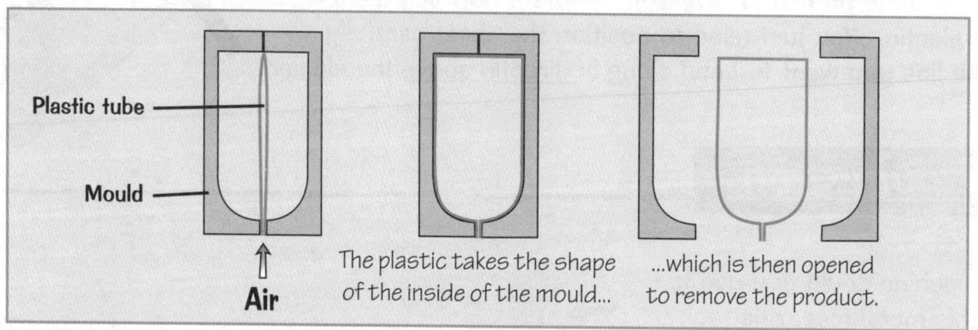

3) This method is often used to produce bottles and containers.

Die Casting Also Uses a Mould

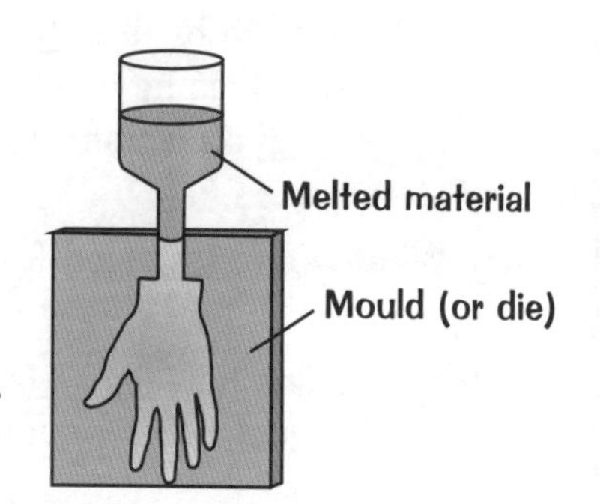

1) Die casting is used to mould metals and thermoplastics.
2) The material is melted and poured into a mould (the 'die') which is in the shape of the product.
3) Some plastic resins can be cold-poured into moulds (without heating). They harden or set through a chemical reaction.

Don't eat this book — because this page is all mouldy...

In both vacuum forming and injection moulding (next page) the moulds must have rounded corners and be slightly tapered (sloped) at the sides — so that the finished product can be released from the mould.

Casting and Moulding

Injection Moulding Uses Pressure to Mould Plastics

1) This is similar to casting, but the molten material is forced into a closed mould under pressure.
2) The moulds are often made from tool steel — so they're quite expensive.
3) The plastic is often melted using built-in heaters.
4) This is an industrial process which is usually automatic and continuous (see page 67).

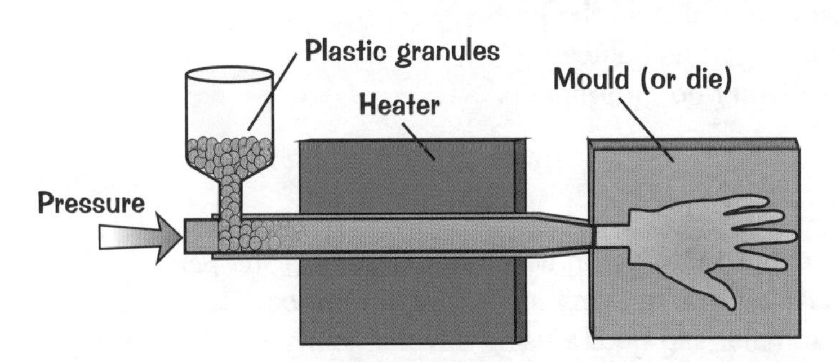

Plastics expert Brian had doubts about his new job.

Extrusion Produces Long, Continuous Strips

1) This process is very similar to injection moulding. It's used for some metals and thermoplastics.
2) The material is melted and forced under pressure through a die.
3) It produces long, continuous strips of the moulding exactly the same shape as the exit hole. It's used for products like plastic-covered wire, and plastic and aluminium edgings.

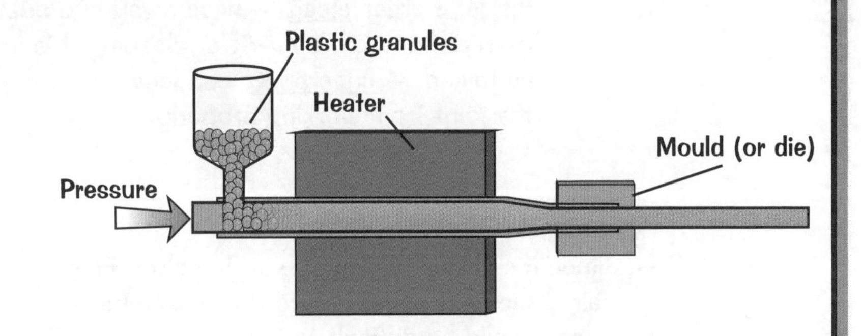

Practice Questions

1) a) What type of material is press moulding used to shape?
   b) Outline what happens during press moulding.

2) Describe the process of vacuum forming.

3) a) What moulding process is often used to make plastic bottles?
   b) Draw diagrams showing how this process could be used to make a plastic bottle.

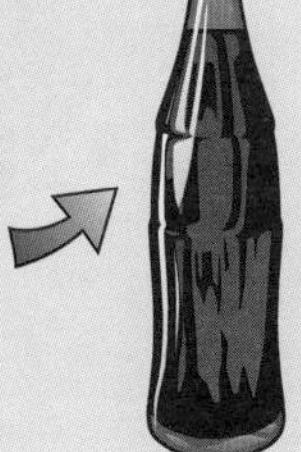

4) a) What is a die?
   b) What types of materials can be moulded using die casting?

5) Peter is making a product using injection moulding.
   a) Suggest what type of material he is using.
   b) Outline the process of injection moulding.

6) Name two products that are made using extrusion moulding.

Assembly and Finishing

Assembly... don't worry, there are no hymns here.

Assembly is Putting the Product Together

But before you put a product together, there are usually some last minute things to do...

1) If you're going to use permanent joining methods, it's vital to double-check the fit of the parts before final assembly. For example, before gluing, make sure you've tried the parts together first in a 'dry run'. This avoids getting halfway through gluing and finding that a part won't go on properly.

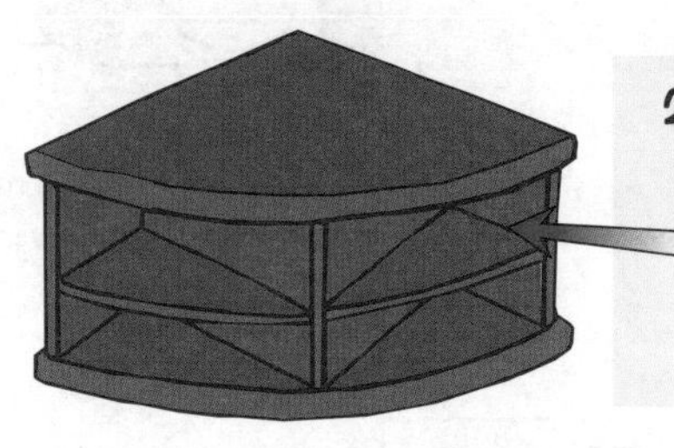

2) Think about the order in which you assemble the parts, especially if you're using a permanent method. For example, say you're using dovetail joints for the shelving in a cabinet. You'd put all the shelves in before you put the top on — or you wouldn't be able to get access.

3) Before gluing, soldering, brazing or welding (see page 32) it's vital to get the joint areas clean — wipe away any dust and make sure they're free from dirt and oil, etc. After cleaning, it's important not to touch areas to be joined — fingerprints can leave enough grease on the surface to stop the joint from working properly.

4) Sometimes it's easier to clean up and apply a finish (e.g. paint, see next page) before final assembly — some areas would be difficult to get at otherwise.

For example, if you're making a box, you might want to paint the inside surfaces before putting it all together.

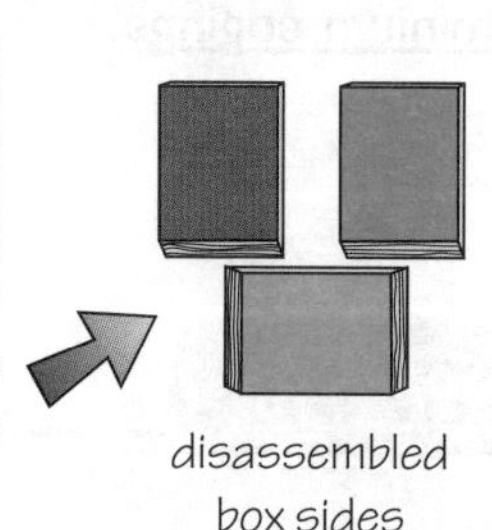

disassembled box sides

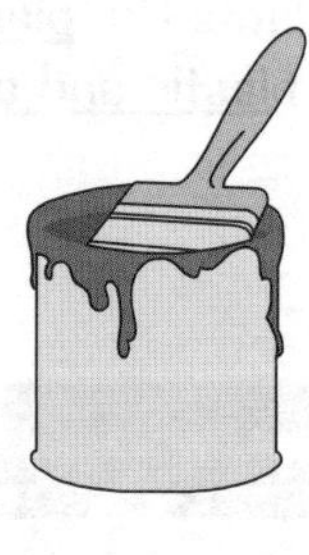

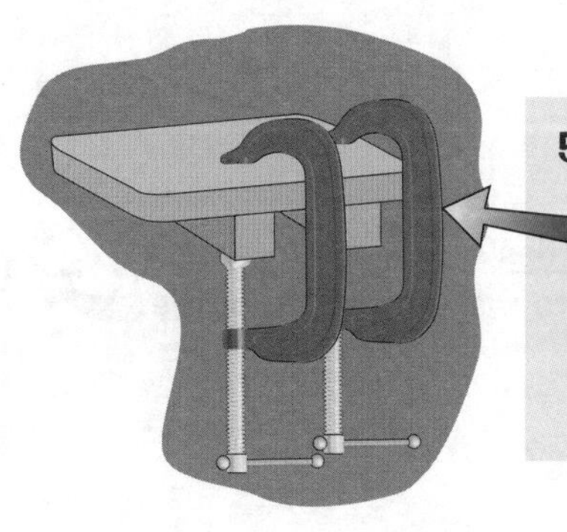

5) Parts that have been glued often need clamping together while the glue dries. Parts that have been soldered, brazed or welded may also need clamping. Removing clamps too early can break the joint. Some glues require the joint to be clamped for 12 hours or more, e.g. acrylic cement (see page 53).

You've not quite finished yet...

Nearing the end of a project is no excuse to start rushing. There are still things that could go wrong — and you wouldn't want to ruin all that hard work. You'll have to write about this stuff in the exam too.

Assembly and Finishing

Finishing Makes the Product Look Pretty

Finishing is the final process in the making of any product. It makes the product look good and protects it from moisture and dirt. Occasionally, the finish is applied before the parts are put together — this is just because it's easier to reach some parts then, e.g. tricky corners.

1) Before finishes are applied it's important to remove any visible tool marks and blemishes with files, emery cloths, glasspaper, etc.

No, not those sort of files...

2) If you're going to paint things, remember to clean the surface first to remove grease and dust. You can do this with white spirit on a cloth.

Cars are often sprayed with cellulose paint.

3) Different paints are produced for different materials and for use in different situations. It's important to select the correct type — otherwise it might not stick to the material, and it could even damage it. You've got to be especially careful when painting some plastics. (See page 41 for more about the best finishes for metals, page 44 for plastics and page 47 for wood.)

4) Cellulose paint is generally applied to metal. It's sprayed on and looks great because it gives a very smooth finish. However, it's expensive because spraying means that much of the paint doesn't end up on the product.

Practice Questions

1) Dave is about to join the parts of his product together. He is going to use a permanent glue. What should he do before he begins?

2) What should be done to prepare material that's going to be joined by welding? Why?

3) Jenny has glued her product. How can she make sure that the parts don't fall apart while the glue is drying?

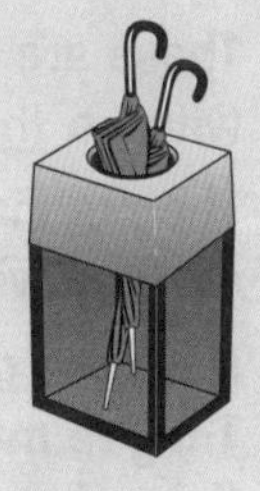

4) Hannah is going to paint her umbrella stand. Why might she decide to paint the parts before assembling the stand?

5) Give two reasons for using finishes on a garden table.

6) Suggest how you could remove tool marks from a surface before applying a finish.

7) Why is it important to select the right type of paint for the material you're using?

8) Jeremy is using cellulose paint to finish his product.
   a) What substance could he use to clean the surface before he paints it?
   b) Suggest what type of material his product is made from.
   c) How is cellulose paint applied?
   d) Why is cellulose paint an expensive choice?

Screws, Bolts and Nails

Screws, bolts and nails can all be used to join materials together. Nails join things permanently, but screws and bolts are non-permanent and can be removed, e.g. if a product needs maintenance.

Screws and Bolts are used with Wood, Metal and Plastic

There are different types of screws for use with wood, metals and plastics.

1) Woodscrews often require 'pilot' holes to be drilled before the screw is inserted. As the screw is turned by a screwdriver, the thread (the twisty bit around the outside of the screw) pulls it into the wood. Different types of head are available for different jobs, e.g. round, countersunk, slotted and cross heads.

2) Self-tapping screws have hardened threads and are designed to cut their own threaded holes in hard materials such as metals and hard plastics.

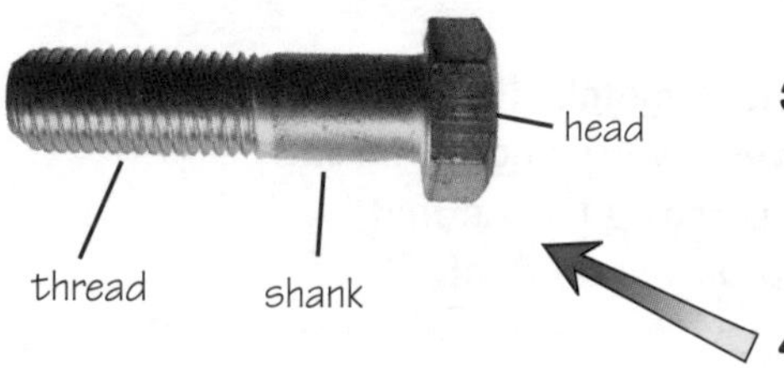

3) Machine screws have a straight shank and are used with washers and nuts. Heads vary (round, countersunk, etc.). Some are tightened with a screwdriver (cross and slotted types), and some with an Allen key (socket head).
4) Bolts are similar to machine screws but have a square or hexagonal head and are tightened with spanners.

5) Screws and bolts are usually made from steel, brass or stainless steel, and are 'self-finished' or plated with zinc, brass, chrome, or black japan (a black varnish).

Nails are Used for Joining Bits of Wood Together

1) These are similar in use to woodscrews but have a straight shank with no thread.
2) They're inserted with a hammer and can be punched below the surface with a nail punch to hide the head.
3) Nails are only used in wood and wooden products, e.g. plywood. They're much quicker to use than screws, but the joint they make is nowhere near as strong.
4) Nails are mostly made from steel, but special ones can be made from other metals, e.g. brass for use in boat building.
5) Like screws, nails come with a variety of head and shank shapes for different uses.

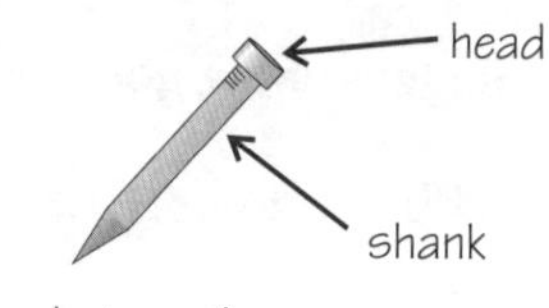

Round wire nail

Don't bite your nails — you'll break your teeth...

Make sure you know the differences between screws, bolts and nails — it's a good start if you can recognise them, but you're on to a winner if you can remember where and how they're used.

Screws, Bolts and Nails

Threaded Joints Don't Need Nuts

1) Threading is a method of fastening machine screws and bolts directly into a metal or plastic component without using nuts.
2) A hole is drilled and a 'tap' is used to cut a female thread in the hole. The screw is inserted into it and tightened until it stops.

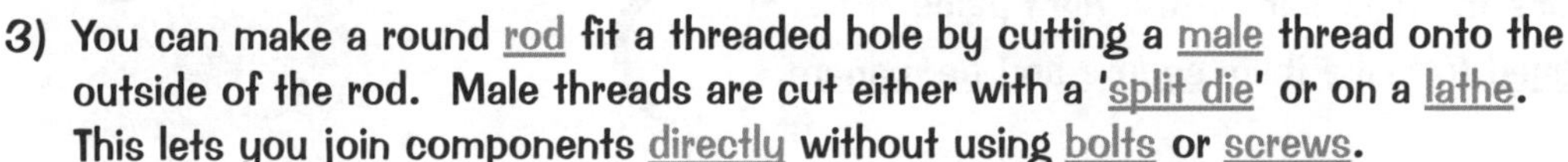

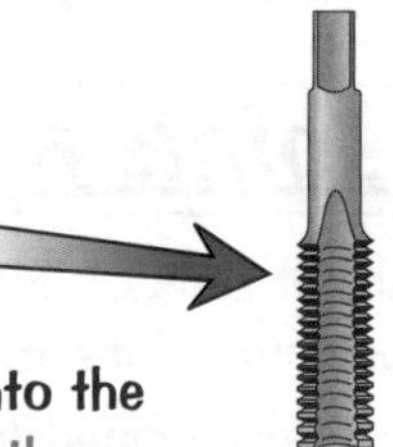

3) You can make a round rod fit a threaded hole by cutting a male thread onto the outside of the rod. Male threads are cut either with a 'split die' or on a lathe. This lets you join components directly without using bolts or screws.

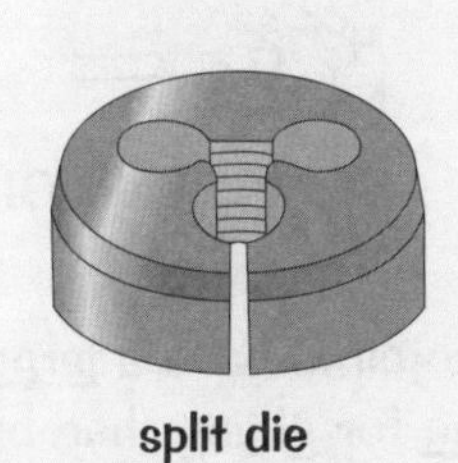

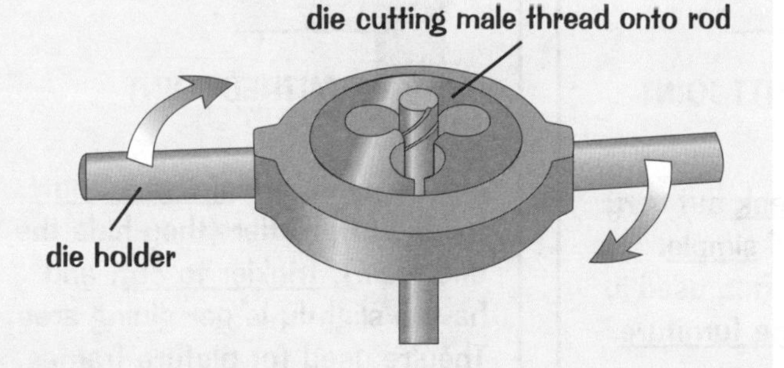

Practice Questions

1) Jim is using screws to join the wood in his product together.
   a) What type of screws should Jim use?
   b) List three different kinds of screw head.
   c) Why might Jim need to use a drill before he can insert a screw?
   d) Jim wants his screw heads to lie as flat as possible against the wood. Which type of screw head should he use — countersunk or round?

2) a) What materials are self-tapping screws used for?
   b) Why are they suitable for these materials?

3) a) The picture on the right shows a machine screw. What other parts are needed when using machine screws?
   b) What tool would be used to tighten this machine screw?

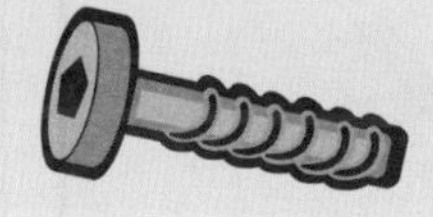

4) a) What is shown in the picture on the left?
   b) What tool is used to tighten it?
   c) Suggest what material it is made from.

5) Nails can be used instead of screws to join pieces of wood together.
   b) Give one advantage of using nails rather than screws.
   c) Give one disadvantage of using nails.

6) a) Explain what is meant by 'threading'.
   b) Outline the process of threading.
   c) Name this tool and say what it's for.

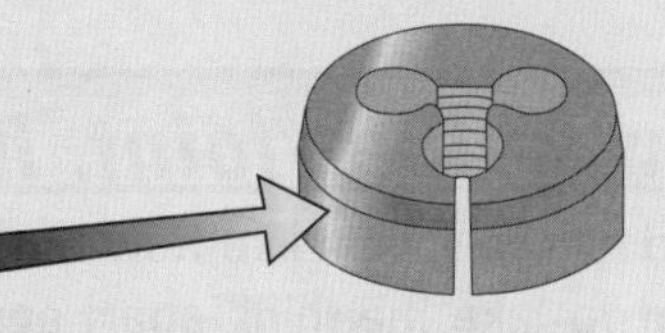

Joints

Wood can be joined together in several ways — either by the traditional method of cutting joints and nailing and gluing together, or by using special fittings which can be taken apart again.

Some Joints are More Permanent than Others

1) There are dozens of different joints for use in different situations. It's important to use the right joint in the right place.
2) Joints are often glued to make them secure and permanent.

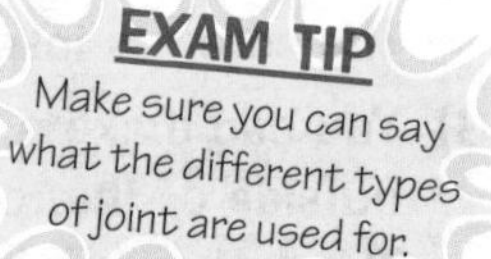

EXAM TIP
Make sure you can say what the different types of joint are used for.

BUTT JOINT

Pretty weak but very quick and simple. They're often used in cheap pine furniture.

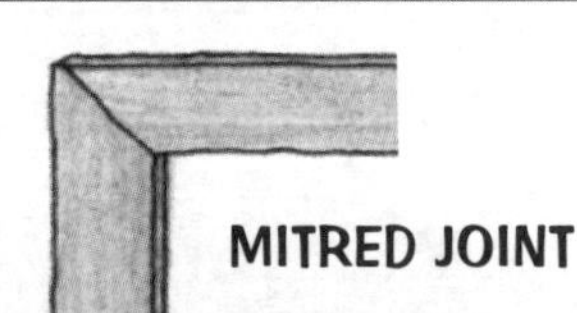

MITRED JOINT

Mitred joints are similar to butt joints but prettier (they hide the end grain), trickier to cut, and have a slightly larger gluing area. They're used for picture frames.

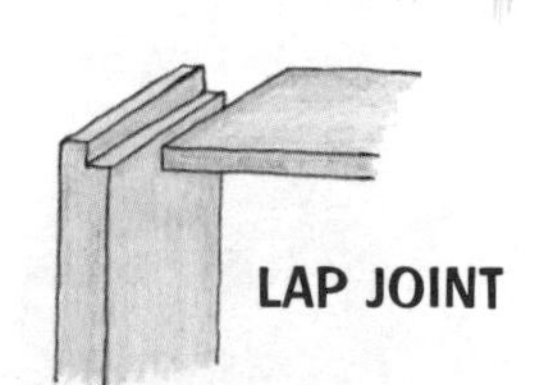

LAP JOINT

Lap joints have a larger surface area for gluing than butt joints, so they're a bit stronger. They're used in some drawers and boxes.

DOWEL JOINT

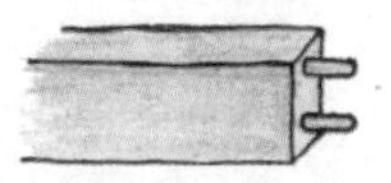
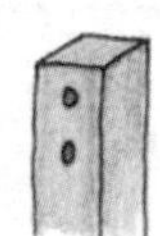

Dowel joints use a wooden or plastic peg, called a dowel, which fits into aligned holes to reinforce the joint. They're often used instead of traditional joints in factory-made furniture.

MORTISE AND TENON

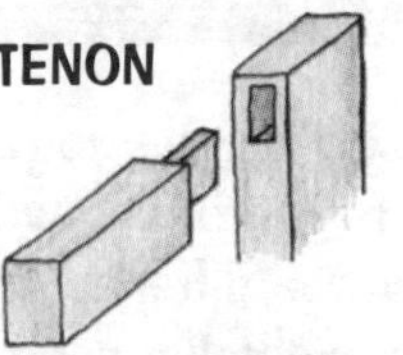

Mortise and tenon joints (cut with a tenon saw and mortise chisel) are dead strong. They're often used in tables and chairs.

HALVING JOINT

Halving joints are fairly strong — again, due to the large surface area for gluing. They're used in frame construction.

HOUSING JOINT

Housing joints are often used in shelving units — they provide a good surface area for gluing, and the shelf is supported all the way along its depth.

DOVETAIL JOINT

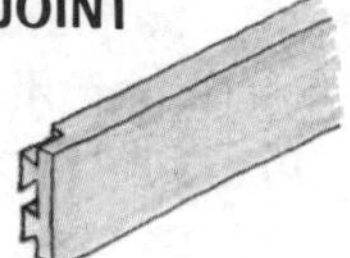

Dovetail joints are very strong and look attractive. They're often used in drawer construction. They're the bee's knees, but they're a pain in the neck to make. Unless you have a dovetail jig (see page 68).

No rude jokes now — butt joint, haha... oh...

Which joint you use comes down to things like how much time you've got, how good you are at woodwork, whether you want to take the thing apart again and how strong you want the joint to be.

Joints

Knock-Down Fittings are Non-Permanent Joints

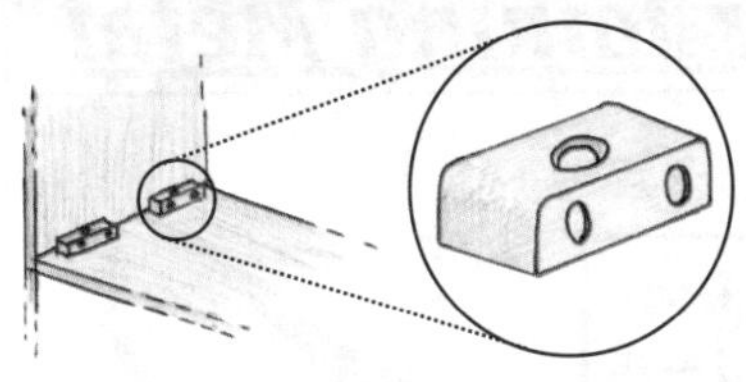

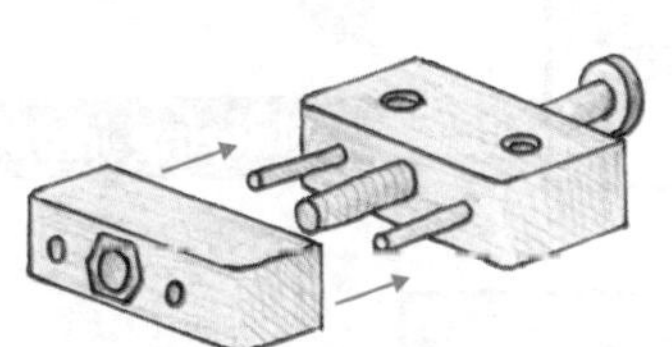

1) These are blocks, brackets (plastic or metal) and other fittings which enable furniture to be assembled and taken apart again easily.
2) They're used instead of traditional joints, and are very fast to use, but are nowhere near as strong as glued joints.
3) Most types are assembled with screwdrivers or Allen keys.
4) They're usually used for cheap 'flat-pack' furniture.

You Need to Choose the Right Adhesive for the Job

1) There are many different types of adhesive for use with different materials and for different jobs, e.g. PVA (for wood), acrylic cement (for plastics) and contact adhesive and epoxy resin (for lots of materials). See pages 52-53 for more about adhesives.
2) Adhesives will only work properly if you choose the right one for the job, and if the surfaces to be joined are really clean.
3) Some plastics can't be glued because they're too smooth, and have a greasy texture which stops the glue from 'keying in'.

You often get a little tube of PVA wood glue with flat-pack furniture to reinforce joints.

Practice Questions

1) Name the types of joint below.

a)

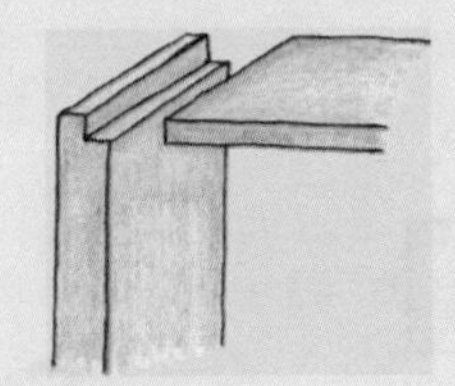

b)

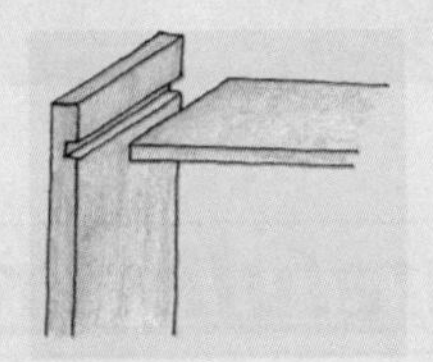

c)

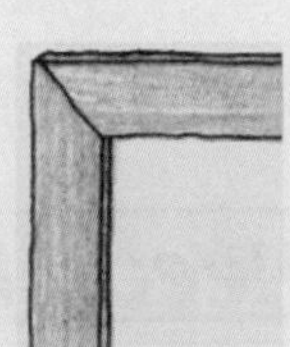

2) Why are halving joints quite strong?
3) What is the disadvantage of using butt joints?
4) John is making a wooden chair. Suggest what type of joint he might use to join the legs to the seat.
5) Dovetail joints are very strong and attractive. Why are they only used in quite expensive furniture?
6) a) What are knock-down fittings?
   b) Give one advantage and one disadvantage of using knock-down fittings.
   c) Where are knock-down fittings often used?
7) Simon is making a plastic clock. He is using adhesive to join the components.
   a) What type of adhesive should he use?
   b) Why are some plastics not suitable for gluing?

Joining Metals

It's the page you've been waiting for — it's all about welding and stuff. Splendid.

Soldering, Brazing and Welding are for Joining Metal

All these methods of joining metals need heat.

1) Soldering is a relatively low temperature process. Solder, made from tin and other metals, is melted onto the components to be joined — it sticks them together when it cools and solidifies. A soldering iron or a blow torch can be used for this process.

soldering iron

blow torch

2) Brazing is a higher temperature process which uses brass spelter as the joining material. It's much stronger than soldering. Either a gas brazing torch, a blow torch, or a brazing attachment for an electric-arc welder is used to heat the joint.

3) Welding is by far the strongest method of joining metal. It uses a very high temperature from an oxyacetylene torch, an electric-arc welder or a laser to actually melt the edges of the joint so that they flow together. Welding can also be used to fill in thinned metal or slight gaps — metal from a welding rod is melted on.

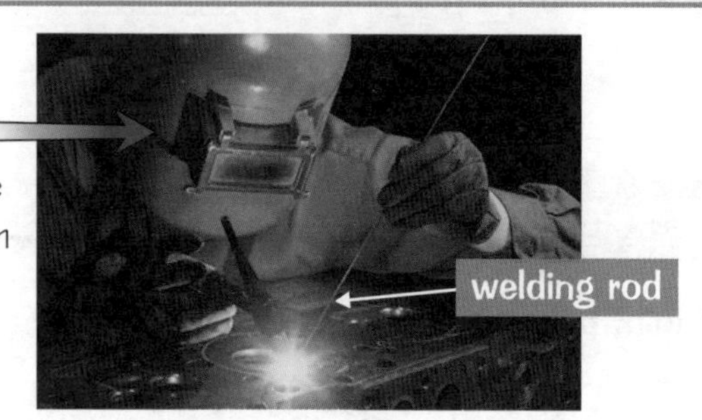

welding mask — to protect your eyes from the bright light and UV radiation from the welding arc. It also protects your face from heat and sparks.

welding rod

The Joint Needs to be Carefully Prepared

For all three of the processes above, careful preparation of the joint is vital:

1) Joints have to be well-fitting with minimal gaps.

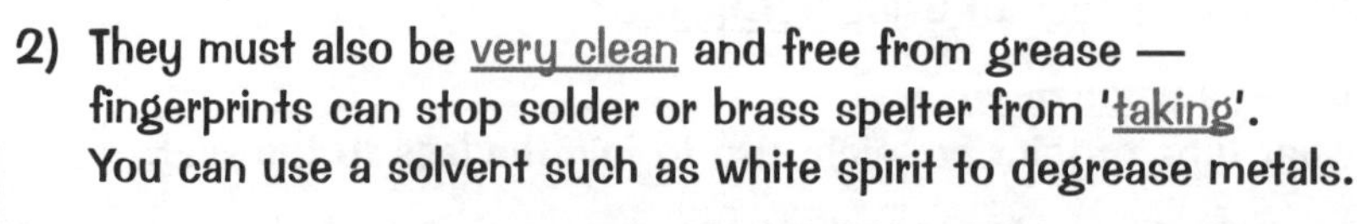

2) They must also be very clean and free from grease — fingerprints can stop solder or brass spelter from 'taking'. You can use a solvent such as white spirit to degrease metals.

doughnut

for when you've finished

3) Flux is a cleaning agent that's used when soldering and brazing and on some metals when welding. It stops the air from oxidising the surface of the metal while you're heating it, as this too would stop the joint from taking.

Only Section 2 — keep soldering on...

So, there are four methods to learn — soldering, brazing, welding and riveting (next page). Oh, and a little bit on how to prepare the metal first. Take it slowly and learn it properly. It's riveting stuff.

Joining Metals

Rivets are Mainly Used for Joining Sheet Metal

1) A rivet is a metal peg with a head on one end. Rivets are mostly used for joining pieces of metal.

2) A hole is drilled through both pieces of metal and the rivet is inserted with a set (hammer-like tool). The head is held against the metal whilst the other end is flattened and shaped into another head with a hammer.
3) 'Pop' (or 'blind') rivets are now very common. They can be used where there is only access to one side of the material (hence 'blind' rivet). It's a fast and easy method of joining sheet metal.

HOW POP RIVETS WORK

① The metal pin is inserted through the hole in the centre of the pop rivet.

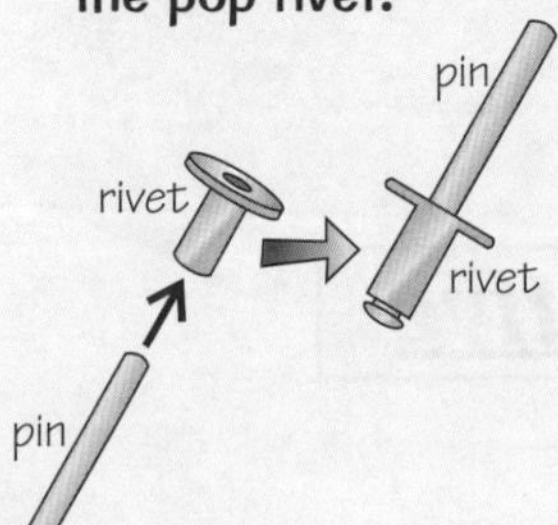

② Both rivet and pin are placed in the hole in the material.

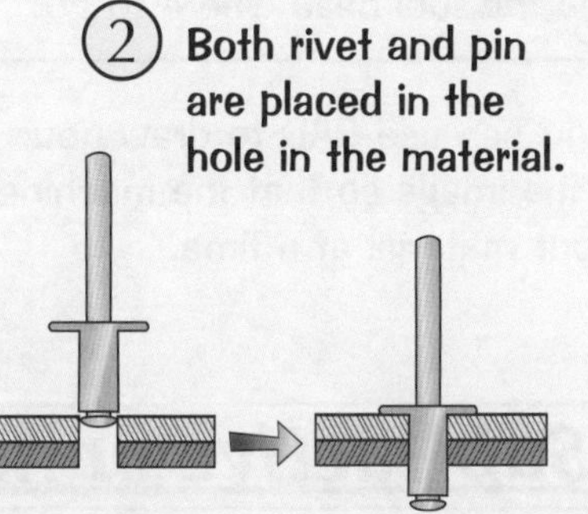

③ The pin is pulled tight with a riveter (or pop gun) till it snaps off.

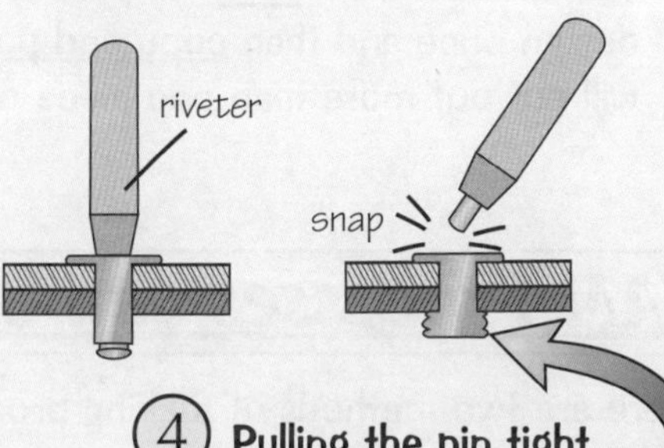

④ Pulling the pin tight makes the end of the rivet expand, forming a head on the 'blind' side.

Practice Questions

1) Which process uses the lowest temperature — soldering, brazing or welding?
2) What is solder made from?
3) a) What is used as the joining material in brazing?
   b) Which makes a stronger joint — soldering or brazing?
   c) Give two tools that could be used to heat the joint when brazing.

4) John is repairing some metal pipes by welding.
   a) Describe what happens to form a joint in welding.
   b) How could thin gaps in metal be closed by welding?
   c) Give a safety precaution that John should take when welding and say why it's necessary.
5) Explain why a joint must be cleaned before brazing.
6) What is flux used for?
7) a) What are rivets used for?
   b) Outline how a rivet is used.
   c) Give one advantage of using pop rivets.
   d) Outline how a pop rivet is used.

CAD/CAM

So, here's a spot of Computer Aided Design and Computer Aided Manufacture, or CAD/CAM to its friends.

CAD/CAM is Designing and Making Using a Computer

1) You can use CAD to draw your designs in 2D and 3D.
2) CAM (Computer Aided Manufacture) takes information from the CAD drawing and manufactures the product for you.

There's more on CAD on p.15.

- The machines used in CAM are Computer Numerically Controlled (CNC).
- This means the CAD/CAM program works out the necessary movements of the tool head and sends instructions to the machine as numbers (the x, y and z coordinates, see page 15). The machine's onboard processor interprets these numbers and tells the tool head where to go.

3) To manufacture a batch of products you can use CAD to draw your design once and then copy and paste the image so that the machines will cut out more than one piece on your material at a time.

EXAM TIP
You might have to explain how CAD/CAM could be used to design and make a product.

CAM Processes can be Subtractive or Additive

There are two methods of making products — subtractive and additive.

Subtractive

1) Subtractive processes are when material is removed from a larger piece of material to create a product.
2) Examples of subtractive CAM systems are CNC routers, milling machines and laser cutting machines.

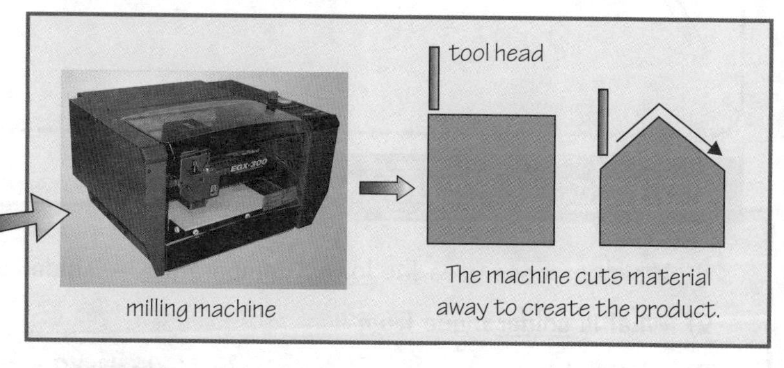

The machine cuts material away to create the product.

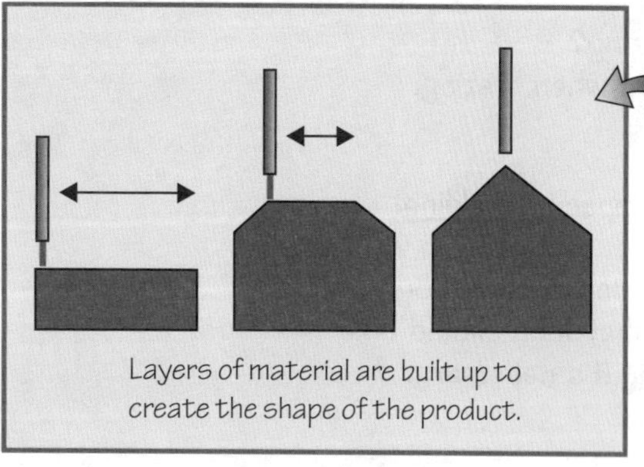
Layers of material are built up to create the shape of the product.

Additive

Additive processes work by adding material to build up the product rather than by removing it. For example:

1) 3D Printing (see next page) works by printing layers of molten plastic, powder or wax until the full 3D shape has been formed.
2) Stereolithography makes 3D products by using a laser beam to 'cure' liquid resin (turn it into a solid) in thin layers. This is pricier and slower than 3D printing.
3) Laser-sintering is similar but the laser fuses powder together instead of curing a liquid. It's quicker than stereolithography but the finish isn't quite so good.

CAD/CAM — for telling tools where to go...

As well as getting your head round what CAD and CAM are, you've also got to know the difference between additive and subtractive processes, and learn about a few machines that do each type.

CAD/CAM

Rapid Prototyping Helps you Model Designs

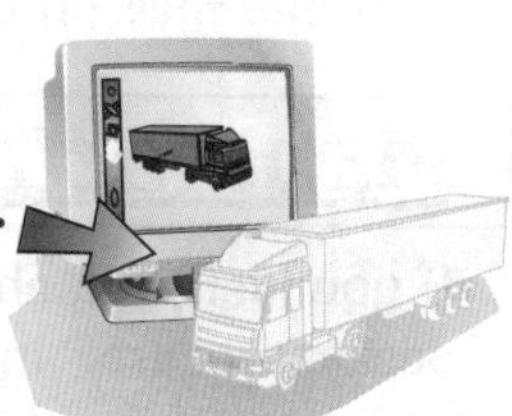

CAD/CAM is useful for making models. You can design on screen then use a rapid prototyping machine — a 3D printer that converts your design into a 3D model. Stereolithography and laser sintering can also be used for rapid prototyping but they're much slower and more expensive.

Using CAD/CAM has Lots of Benefits and Few Drawbacks

It's very expensive to buy and set up CAD/CAM systems, but they save money in the long run. CAD/CAM has lots of benefits for designers and manufacturers in many different industries. For example:

It's easy to develop and edit 2D and 3D images of your design ideas and view them from all angles. It's easy to experiment with different materials and finishes.

Designers can produce very realistic designs quickly on screen, which helps their boss or the client to understand what the designer is proposing. Once a design is finalised, CAD can be used to produce the final presentation drawing with all the finishes, as well as an exploded view (see page 14) of all the parts.

Products can be machined at high speed, and the machines can run 24 hours a day — so loads of things can be manufactured in a short time. Machines can also work in conditions that would be hazardous to people, e.g. paint spraying.

Car bodies are made using CAM.

CAM gives a high quality and more reliable finish — there's no human error involved.

You can mass-produce complicated products. Each part can be manufactured by a different machine and the parts can be assembled quickly.

Labour costs are lower — machines are doing almost all the work.

But computers can be affected by software problems, viruses, and corrupted files — potentially slowing down production.

Because fewer workers are needed, unemployment might increase and traditional skills could be lost.

Practice Questions

1) What does CNC stand for?
2) a) What is the difference between an additive process and a subtractive process?
   b) Give two examples of subtractive CAM systems.
   c) Give two examples of additive CAM systems.
3) a) Outline how a rapid prototyping machine works.
   b) At what stage of design and manufacture would you use rapid prototyping?
4) Explain three benefits of using CAD/CAM in the design and manufacture of products.

Quality Assurance and Control

Quality assurance (QA) is the systems and procedures that manufacturers have in place to make sure that their products are high quality.

Manufacturers Want Customer Satisfaction

If you just think about design as what you do in D&T lessons, you might see evaluation as the end of the design process. In industry, the end of the process is customer satisfaction...

See pages 10-11 for more on evaluation.

> Customer satisfaction is achieved when the product works, is great to use, and is good value for money.

The way to make this happen is to make sure your product is high quality. You can also use customer feedback (what users of the product think) to check whether your customers are satisfied.

Quality Assurance is an Overall System

1) Top companies that do QA well are awarded ISO 9000 — an international standard of quality management.
2) QA includes having good staff training, procedures for checking the quality of materials and systems for keeping machinery maintained.
3) It also includes quality control checks throughout the manufacturing process — see below.
4) So when you're planning a manufacturing process (for your project or in the exam) remember to work in quality checks at every stage — see pages 16-17.

The aim of all this is to ensure that products:

1) conform to the specification
2) do the job they were designed to do
3) meet the standards set down by the relevant institutions
   E.g. the British Standards Institution or the British Electrotechnical Approvals Board.
4) keep the customer happy
5) are manufactured consistently
   Using templates and jigs (see page 68) and CAD/CAM helps to make sure that products are consistent. This is particularly important in batch production.

Quality Control Means Checking Components

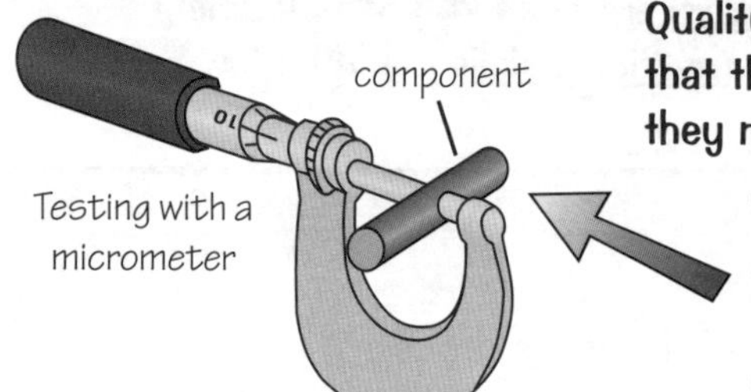

Testing with a micrometer

Quality control means testing samples of components to check that they meet the manufacturer's specification. For example, they must be the right colour or the right size.

When components are checked for size they must be within a specific tolerance. Tolerance is given as an upper (+) and lower (–) limit for the measurement. For example, if a component should have a diameter of 20 mm (±0.5), then a micrometer reading of 19.9 mm would be ok but 20.7 mm would not.

Tolerance — needed when you've got revision to do...

I guess customer satisfaction would be buying this book but not having to spend hours revising from it. Sorry, but if you want to give high quality answers in the exam you need to do high quality revision.

Quality Assurance and Control

There are Different Kinds of Testing

Failures at testing can identify faults with machining and tool settings and eliminate costly waste. Once you've spotted a problem you can put it right.

1) Measuring components with a micrometer is a time-consuming (and therefore costly) business. The process can be speeded up using limit gauges. These are usually double-ended, one end being machined to the lower limit and the other end to the upper limit.

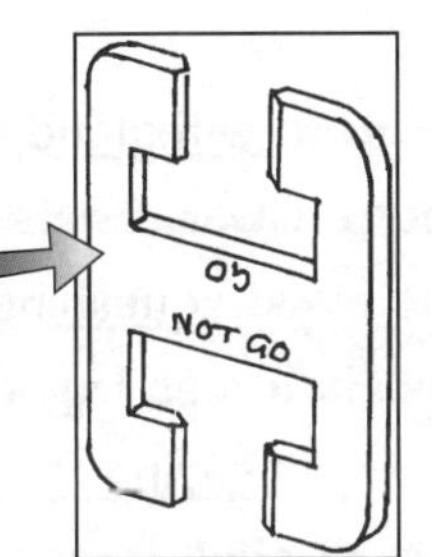

If the component fits through the upper limit but not the lower one, it's within the acceptable range.

2) Some testing is visual and may include using X-rays to spot defects, e.g. cracks in a welded joint. This is non-destructive testing.

Tom's destructive testing went a bit too far.

3) Some testing is physical and destroys the product to see when and how it fails. This is destructive testing. It helps manufacturers to write safety instructions for their products — e.g. how heavy a load the product can take.

Practice Questions

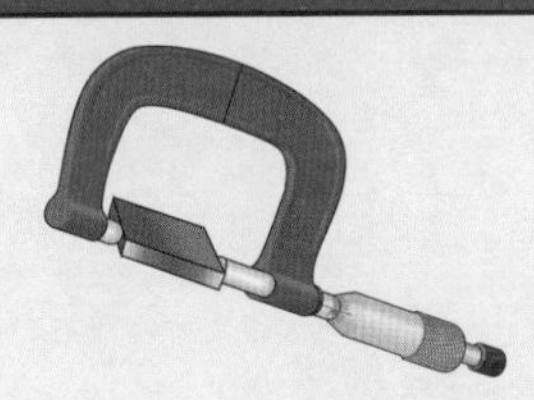

1) Why is it important to make sure that products are high quality?
2) What is ISO 9000?
3) What is the name of the tool on the left?
4) A part that should measure 21 mm could actually be up to 3 mm longer or shorter. How would this tolerance be written in the specification?
5) Sally is making a picture frame. The frame must have a thickness of 25 mm (±0.4). Would the following measurements be acceptable for this component?
   a) 25.2 mm
   b) 25.5 mm
   c) 24.8 mm
   d) 24.5 mm
6) Why are limit gauges useful?
7) Pierre has made an Eiffel-Tower-themed table from steel. He is testing the table.
   a) Why might he use X-rays?
   b) Pierre's boss thinks he should do a destructive test of the table's strength. Describe how Pierre could do this destructive testing.
   c) What would be the point of doing this destructive test?

Properties of Materials

Different Materials Have Different Properties

Make sure you're really familiar with all these terms — if you start getting strength and hardness mixed up, or get confused between malleable and ductile, you'll be dropping marks all over the place.

STRENGTH

Strength is the ability to withstand forces without breaking. For example:

1) The rope in a tug-of-war resists pulling forces.
2) Bridge supports resist squashing forces.
3) A surfboard resists forces trying to bend it.
4) A rivet resists strong sliding forces.
5) A drill bit resists twisting forces.

HARDNESS

1) This is the ability to withstand scratching, rubbing or denting.
2) It's very important for tools that cut, like files and drills.

PLASTICITY

1) If a material can change shape permanently, without breaking or cracking, it's said to have good plastic qualities.
2) This could mean that the material is malleable (can be moulded, e.g. by hammering) or ductile (can be drawn into wires).

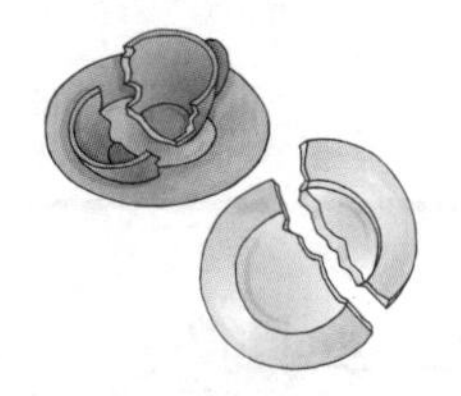

BRITTLENESS

1) Brittle materials can't withstand much stretching.
2) Brittle materials are more likely to crack or break than change their shape.
3) Glass is brittle.

TOUGHNESS

1) Tough is the opposite of brittle.
2) If a material is tough, it can absorb impacts without breaking or snapping.
3) Armour and bulletproof vests need to be tough.

EXAM TIP
You get marks for explaining why a particular material is suitable for a product. E.g. 'because it's durable'.

DURABILITY

1) If a product is durable it's able to withstand repeated use.
2) Durable products also withstand wear and tear and corrosion.

Some live in bungalows, some in semi-detached...

Property jokes aside, you need to be able to say why a material is suitable for a product, and there's only one way you can do that... you really need to get your head around what all these terms mean.

Properties of Materials

There are Other Factors to Think About Too...

When it comes to choosing which material to use in a product, there's a lot to consider:

FUNCTIONAL REQUIREMENTS

1) What demands will be made on the material? For example, it might have to hold heavy loads.
2) Will it be used outdoors or indoors? You'll need to consider whether your material will corrode.
3) Does it need to fit in with an environment? It might need a certain look.

AVAILABILITY

Can you get the material you want in a suitable form? Most materials are only available in standard forms and sizes — it can be very expensive to get them in other forms. This will have a direct effect on the cost and the method of manufacture.

For example, materials might be available as granules, strips, bars, tubes, rough sawn, planed...

PRODUCTION METHOD

1) Some materials are easier to join than others. For example, you can't just glue bits of metal together as you can with wood.
2) The material must be suitable for the intended production method (and vice versa). For example, you can use injection moulding with plastics but certainly not with wood.

ECONOMICS

1) You need to think about the size of the product — materials like pewter are expensive, but may be a good choice for a small item of jewellery.
2) Whether your product is a one-off, or will be batch or mass produced (see p.66-67) will make a difference.

If you're making a one-off hand crafted piece of furniture you might use an expensive piece of hardwood. However, if you're batch producing cheap furniture, softwood would probably be fine.

Practice Questions

1) Describe what is meant by the following properties:
   a) brittle b) malleable c) ductile
2) Suggest a product that needs to be:
   a) hard b) durable c) tough
3) List three products for which strength is important, and say why.
4) The size of a product can affect what material you'd make it from. Explain why.

5) Some products are batch produced and others are one-offs. How might this affect the materials that are used?
6) Cho is designing a slide for a playground. She is deciding whether to make it from plastic or metal.
   a) Suggest the properties that the material needs to have.
   b) Explain why Cho should consider the manufacturing method before choosing a material.
   c) Why does Cho need to think about the shapes of materials available?

Metals

Metals Come From the Ground...

Ore contains the metal along with other substances.

Metal is mined as metal ore. This is processed and refined to make a usable material. The process isn't the same for all metals, but it's often like this:

1) The ore is crushed and heated with other materials in a blast furnace. This process separates the metal from the other substances in the ore. The metal is removed from the blast furnace as molten metal.

2) The molten metal is poured into a casting machine where it's cooled and run through rollers to make blocks. These can then be made into various different shapes (see page 43).
3) The molten metal from the blast furnace still has some impurities. For some uses you need really pure metal — so sometimes the metal is refined to remove these impurities.

...And This Can Harm the Environment

1) Digging up metals disfigures the landscape.
2) Processing and refining metals causes pollution — the chemicals used can be harmful, especially if they get into water sources.
3) Transporting great truckloads of metal ore also causes air and noise pollution.
4) Metal products are often disposed of in landfill sites — more metal will need to be extracted from the ground. Instead we could recycle and reuse metals:

- Recycling uses less energy than extracting new metal and produces less pollution. All good.
- Metals can also be reused. E.g. parts from scrapped cars can be used to fix other cars.
- Metal ores are a finite resource (they'll run out eventually) so recycling and reusing metals is a great idea.

Heat Treatments Soften or Toughen Metals

Metals can be heat-treated to change their properties. There are three main types of treatment:

1) Annealing — heating the metal and leaving it to cool slowly. This makes it softer, more ductile and less brittle.
2) Hardening — heating and rapidly cooling a metal. This makes it, erm... harder.
   The metal is heated till it's red hot then plunged into cold water or oil.
   This leaves the metal brittle, so hardening is often followed by tempering...
3) Tempering — to make the metal tougher and less likely to break.
   When steel is tempered, it's first cleaned (to make it bright in appearance) and then gently heated. As it gets hotter, it gradually changes colour — and the colour shows how tough it's become.

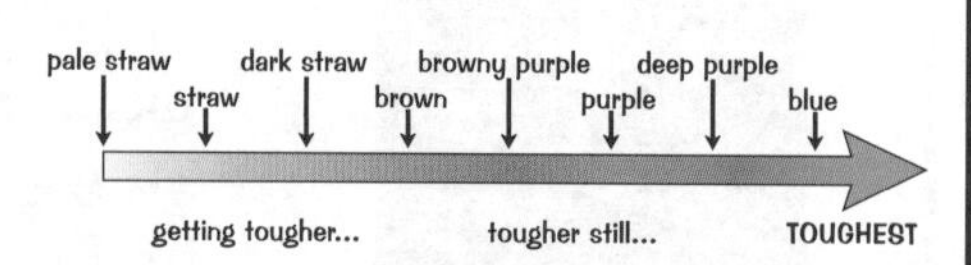

Recycling — riding your bike back the way you came...

There's a mix of stuff on this page — where metals come from, their environmental impact and some hot stuff on heat treatments. Test yourself by seeing how much of this page you can scribble down.

Metals

Metals Can be Finished for Protection and Looks

You need to know about a few different kinds of surface finish...

1) PAINTING

A primer such as red oxide or zinc chromate is needed for steel (so that later coats of paint can form a strong bond to the surface). After the primer you need a top coat. A range of colours and finishes are available. Some types are especially quick drying and some give a very durable, weatherproof finish for outdoor use.

This bridge has been painted a nice shade of red to protect it from rusting in the rain.

2) PLASTIC COATING

A metal is heated evenly in an oven and then plunged into fluidised powder (very fine powder that's made to act like a liquid by passing gas through it) for a few seconds. The metal, with this thin coating of plastic, is then put back in the oven and the plastic fuses (joins completely) to the surface.

Aahhh, shiny, shiny polished chrome...

3) POLISHING

You can do this by hand or by using a buffing wheel — the wheel is coated with abrasive polish and the metal is held against the spinning wheel until the required surface finish is achieved.

Abrasive polishes work by rubbing away the surface.

4) LACQUERING

A thin layer of cellulose, gum or varnish is applied to leave a transparent coating. This provides a barrier against tarnishing and oxidising, and is often used on decorative items such as jewellery.

Tarnishing and oxidising make the metal look dull.

Practice Questions

1) What is a metal ore?
2) Explain how metal ore is processed into usable metal.
3) Why are metals sometimes refined after the initial processing?
4) Give three reasons why extracting metals is harmful to the environment.
5) Explain why it's a good idea to reuse and recycle metals.
6) Explain the differences between annealing and hardening.
7) a) What is the name of the process used to toughen metal?
   b) Outline what happens during the process.
8) Most metal products have their surfaces finished.
   a) Explain why the metal used to make car bodywork is painted.
   b) Describe three other surface finishes used on metals.
   c) For each surface finish you've listed for (b), give an example of a product where this might be used.

Metals

Some metals are pure metals and others (alloys) are mixtures of different metals.
Both types of metal can be classified into two basic groups — ferrous and non-ferrous.

Ferrous Metals Contain Iron

1) These are the metals that contain iron.
2) Because of this, almost all of them are magnetic.
3) Examples include mild steel, high-carbon steel and stainless steel.

EXAM TIP
You might need to suggest a suitable metal for a product, so make sure you know what their properties are.

METAL	PROPERTIES	USES
MILD STEEL	Quite strong and cheap but rusts easily and can't be hardened or tempered.	car bodies, screws, nuts, bolts, nails, washing machines
HIGH-CARBON STEEL	Harder than mild steel and can be hardened and tempered. But it's not as easy to work and it rusts.	drills, files, chisels, saws
STAINLESS STEEL	Hard and won't rust, but is more expensive.	medical equipment, sinks, kettles, cutlery (e.g. knives)

Non-Ferrous Metals Don't Contain Iron *(surprise surprise...)*

1) If a metal doesn't contain iron, it's non-ferrous.
2) Examples include aluminium, brass and copper.

METAL	PROPERTIES	USES
ALUMINIUM	Lightweight and corrosion-resistant but expensive and not as strong as steel	aeroplanes, cans, ladders
BRASS	Quite strong, corrosion-resistant, malleable, ductile and looks good	door handles, electrical parts
COPPER	Relatively soft, malleable and ductile and a very good electrical conductor	wiring, pipes

An Alloy is a Mixture

1) An alloy is a mixture of two or more metals, or a metal mixed with another element (e.g. carbon).
2) Steel is made from a mixture of iron and carbon, and brass is made from copper and zinc.
   Different types of steel (e.g. mild steel and stainless steel) also contain varying quantities of other metals, such as chromium — but you don't need to worry about the details.
3) The alloy is a new material — it has different properties and working characteristics.

Ferrous, not ferrets — easy mistake to make...

Not too much to fret over here — ferrous metals, non-ferrous metals and alloys. Make sure you learn what they are, then learn the names and properties of a few of each, and what they can be used for.

Metals

You Can Buy Metals in Loads of Shapes and Sizes

1) Metals are commonly available in a wide range of shapes and sizes, because it can be very difficult to convert one shape to another.
2) This means that the manufacturers can buy roughly the right shape to start working with.

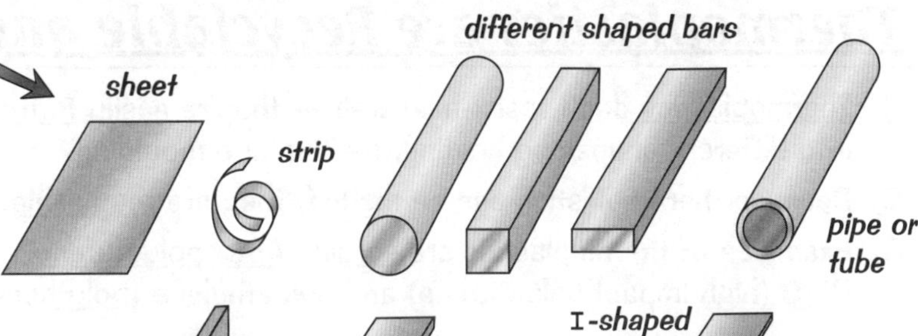

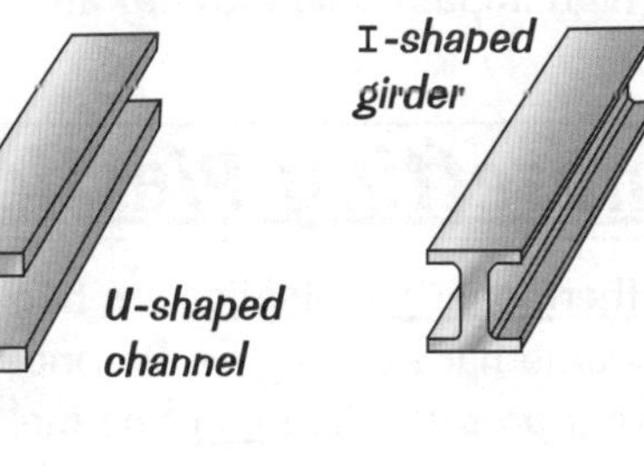

For example...

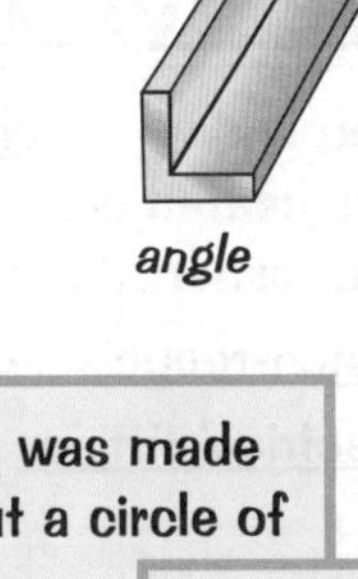

this table top was made by cutting out a circle of sheet metal...

...and the chair legs were made from tubes of metal.

Practice Questions

1) What is a ferrous metal?
2) Name two ferrous metals.
3) Name two non-ferrous metals.
4) Explain why steel is an alloy.
5) Name an alloy other than steel.
6) List five different shapes of metal that are available to manufacturers.
7) Do you think copper would be a suitable material for making the wiring for an electric kettle? Explain your answer.
8) Suggest what material was used to make the head of this hammer. Explain your answer.
9) Explain why stainless steel is useful for making products that are used outdoors.

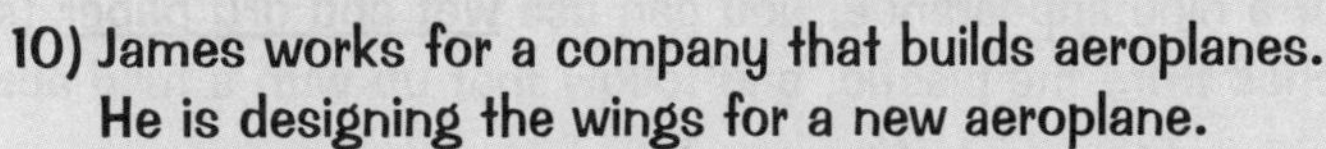

10) James works for a company that builds aeroplanes. He is designing the wings for a new aeroplane.
    a) Suggest a suitable material for the wings. Explain your answer.
    b) As well as its properties, what else might James need to consider when choosing a suitable material?

Plastics

There are two happy families of plastics — thermoplastics and thermosetting plastics.
They've got different properties, so don't go mixing them up — some of them are well 'ard.

Thermoplastics are Recyclable and Bendy

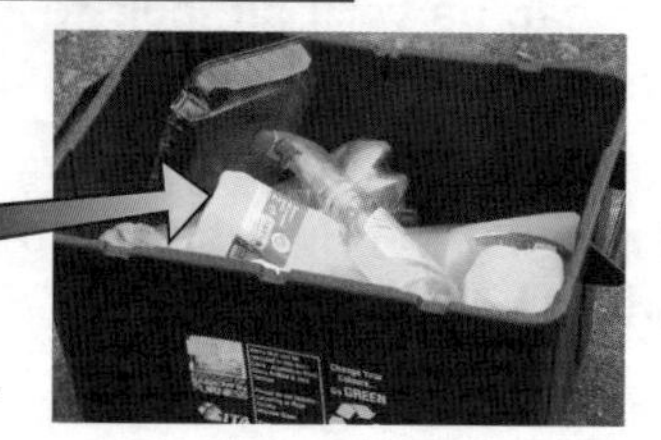

1) Thermoplastics don't resist heat well — they're easily formed into different shapes by heating, melting and moulding.
2) Because thermoplastics can be melted, they are recyclable.
3) Examples of thermoplastics are acrylic, ABS, polystyrene, HIPS (high impact polystyrene) and polyethylene (polythene).

Thermosetting Plastics are Non-Recyclable and Rigid

1) When thermosetting plastics are heated they undergo a chemical change and become hard and rigid. So once you've heated and moulded them to make a product they can't be melted and reshaped again.
2) This means that thermosetting plastics are non-recyclable.
3) They resist heat and fire so are used for electrical fittings and pan handles.
4) Examples of thermosetting plastics are melamine-formaldehyde, polyester resin, epoxy resin and urea-formaldehyde.

EXAM TIP
Don't just write 'plastic' if you're asked to suggest a suitable material — give a specific example, e.g. acrylic.

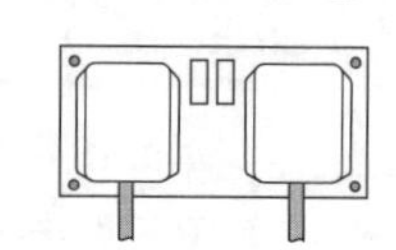

urea-formaldehyde

melamine-formaldehyde

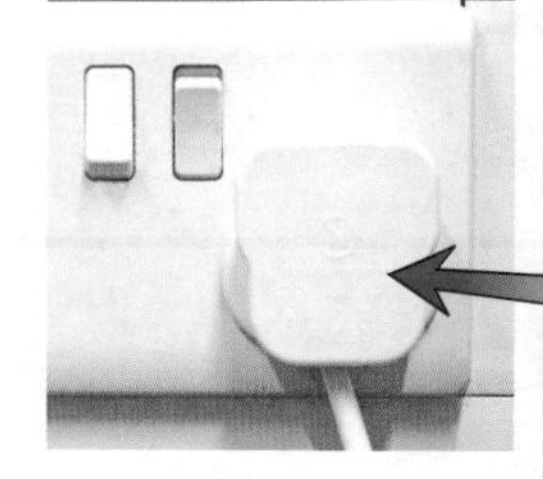

So, which type of plastic you use depends on what you want to do with it.

1) For example, thermosetting plastics are often used where there is heat or electricity involved, or when something needs to be really hard.
2) Different types of thermoplastics have different properties — polypropylene will bend without breaking and is used for plastic chairs so they're comfy when you lean back.

Thermoplastics and thermosetting plastics can be bought in many different forms — from powders, granules, pellets and liquids (for processing into finished products), through to films, sheets, rods, tubes and extruded mouldings (complex shapes).

Plastics Don't Need Surface Finishes

1) Plastics don't need protective surface finishes because they're very resistant to corrosion and decay.
2) But for a nice appearance, you can use wet and dry paper (silicon carbide paper) to remove scratches from the plastic, and follow that up with a mild abrasive polish or anti-static cream.
3) Or, you could use a buffing machine.

Wet and dry paper — sounds like someone's a bit confused...

So, there are two types of plastic that you need to know about — thermoplastics and thermosetting plastics. Small difference in name, but a pretty big difference in their properties. Best get it learnt...

Plastics

Most Plastics Are Made From Oil

Plastics can be made from substances found in plants. This is quite a new thing though. Most plastics are still made from crude oil.

1) Crude oil is extracted from the ground and taken to a refinery.
2) In the refinery, the oil is processed to make various different substances.
3) Some of these substances are then used to make different types of plastic.

Using Plastics Brings Environmental Problems

1) Crude oil is a finite resource — it's going to run out one day. At the moment we're using it up more and more quickly, to make all the plastic stuff we use (and to make fuels).
2) Turning crude oil into plastic uses a lot of energy (which often comes from burning even more oil).
3) Plastics are mostly disposed of in landfill sites. They're buried and take hundreds of years to degrade (break down). Not so good.
4) Some plastics (mainly the ones made from plants) are biodegradable — they break down quickly.
5) Still, it's better to recycle and reuse plastics as much as possible. It means there's less need to make new plastic from oil.

RECYCLING PLASTICS

1) Thermosetting plastics can't be recycled.
2) Thermoplastics can be cleaned, shredded, melted and made into new products.
3) They have to be sorted into the different types by hand (different types are stamped with different symbols to help). This takes time and people are trying to come up with easier, mechanical ways to sort plastics.

REUSING PLASTICS

1) Some plastic products like milk crates and carrier bags can be used over and over again. Things like printer cartridges can be refilled.
2) Reusing doesn't usually use any energy or new materials. Thumbs up.

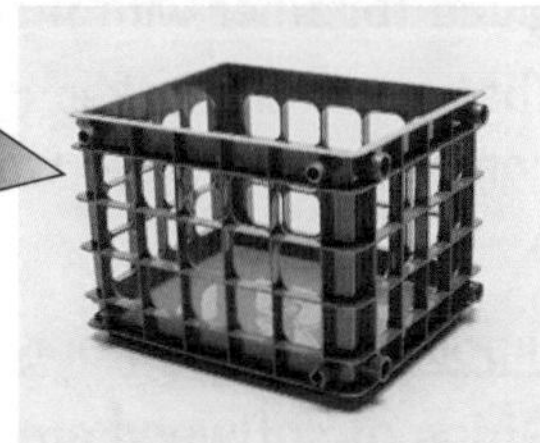

Practice Questions

1) Why are thermosetting plastics non-recyclable?
2) a) Give an example of a thermoplastic.
   b) Give an example of a thermosetting plastic.
3) Rachel is designing a saucepan. Suggest a suitable plastic she could use to make the knob on the lid. Explain your answer.

4) List five of the different forms that plastics can be bought in.
5) John is making a child's toy using epoxy resin.
   a) Explain why epoxy resin doesn't need a protective surface finish.
   b) How could John remove any scratches from the surface of the epoxy resin?
6) Outline how most plastics are made.
7) Describe two environmental problems associated with using plastic.

Wood and Boards

I love trees. Not only can you climb them but you can turn them into timber and boards.

Softwoods are Evergreen Trees, like Pine

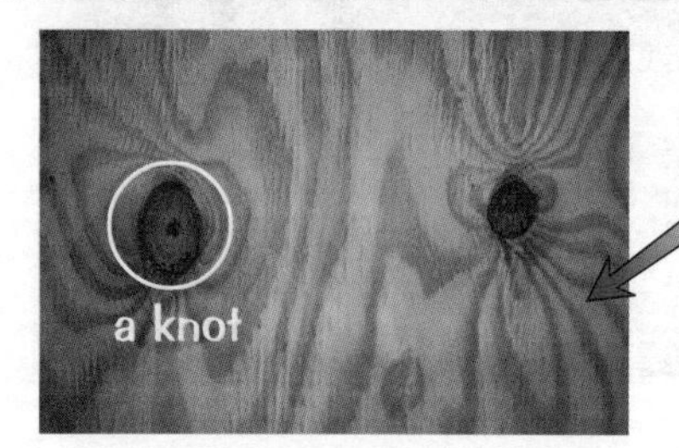

1) Softwoods include pine, cedar and yew.
2) There are several types of pine but they're all generally pale with brown streaks. Scots pine is fairly strong but knotty. Parana pine is more expensive — it's hard and is best used for interior joinery.
3) Softwoods grow in colder climates and are fast growing — this makes them fairly cheap.

Hardwoods are Deciduous Trees, like Oak

1) Hardwoods include oak, mahogany, beech and elm.
2) They usually grow in warm climates and are slow growing — so they're generally more expensive than softwoods.

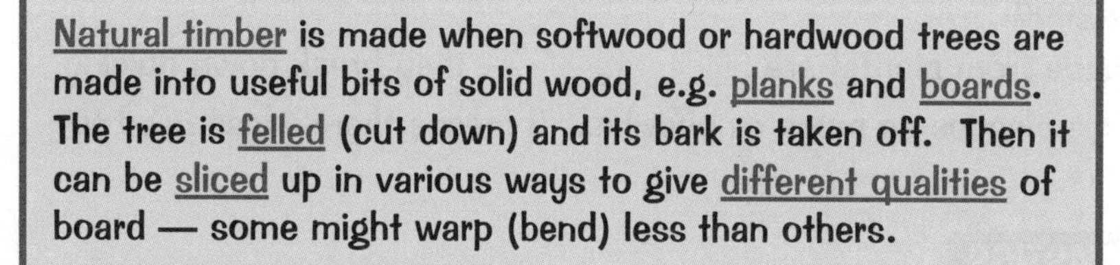
Natural timber is made when softwood or hardwood trees are made into useful bits of solid wood, e.g. planks and boards. The tree is felled (cut down) and its bark is taken off. Then it can be sliced up in various ways to give different qualities of board — some might warp (bend) less than others.

EXAM TIP
You might have to look at a photo and say what type of wood a product is made from — don't just say 'wood'.

Boards Can be Manufactured

Plywood is a very popular manufactured board, used for building and furniture.

1) It's made up of several layers of softwood or hardwood, glued together with their grain at right angles.
2) That structure makes it very strong for its weight and thickness, compared with solid wood.

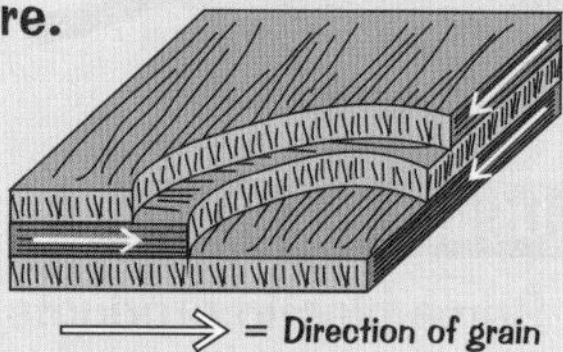

Blockboard isn't as strong as plywood, but it's a cheap substitute. It's often used for doors.

1) Strips of softwood are glued together side by side and sandwiched between two veneers. The veneers add strength and make the board look nicer.
2) The outer veneers are glued with their grain at right angles to the grain of the inner core — this makes it stronger.

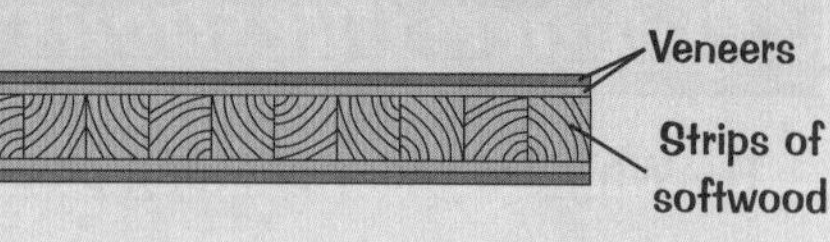

Chipboard is made by compressing wood chips together with glue. It's cheap but not very strong, so it's usually used with a stronger veneered surface. It's often used in cheap self-assembly furniture.

Medium density fibreboard (MDF) is made from even tinier wood particles, glued and compressed. It's pretty cheap and has smooth faces that are easy to paint. MDF is often used for shelving units.

I'm bored — and it's been manufactured by examiners...

Make sure you know the difference between hardwoods and softwoods. Then, once you've got your head around that, there's also the difference between natural timber and manufactured boards. Fun.

Wood and Boards

Like metal, wood is often coated with a finish to protect it and make it look nice.

Wood Can be Protected With Finishes

Most woods need protection, particularly if they're going to be used outdoors.

1) You can apply woodstain to wood to enhance the appearance of its grain. It's available in natural colours but also in bright blues, reds, etc. Stains don't usually protect the wood, so you might need to apply varnish afterwards.
2) Oil can be used to maintain the wood's natural appearance. Some oil-based finishes also offer protection to wood used outdoors.
3) Paint is often used to colour and protect wood. Emulsion paints are cheap, but they are water-based, so they don't protect wood from water. Polyurethane paint is more expensive but is waterproof and much tougher.
4) Polyurethane varnish can be used to seal and protect the surface of the wood, and give it a smooth surface finish. You can buy it clear or in a wide range of colours.

Most hardwoods have an attractive grain — so you might want to use clear varnish rather than paint as a surface finish, e.g. oak furniture is often varnished.

Wood Can be Recycled and Reused

Although wood is sustainable (you can plant new trees) it's still a good idea to reuse and recycle timber. This saves on the energy that's needed for processing trees into new timber.

1) Wood can be shredded and reused to make things like compost, playground flooring or chipboard.
2) Good quality wood (e.g. undamaged floorboards) can be cleaned up and reused — this is called reclaimed wood.
3) However, manufactured boards are pretty tricky to recycle because they've got glue in them — recycling them is a long process and it's quite expensive.

Practice Questions

1) Give an example of a softwood.
2) Give an example of a hardwood.
3) Why are hardwoods generally more expensive than softwoods?
4) What is the difference between natural timber and manufactured board?
5) Blockboard is a type of manufactured board.
   a) Sketch a diagram to show its construction.
   b) List two other types of manufactured board.
   c) Suggest a common use for each type of board you listed in (b).
   d) Why are manufactured boards difficult to recycle?
6) Woods can be protected by painting them.
   a) Suggest what type of wood was used to make this table.
   b) Why might the table have been coated in clear varnish rather than paint?

7) Explain why wood is a sustainable resource.
8) Suggest two ways in which wood can be reused.

Composites and New Materials

With composites and 'smart materials' you can make products that weren't possible before, or much better versions of existing products.

A Composite is a Combination of Two or More Materials

1) Composite materials are made from two or more materials bonded together.
2) This can make a material with more useful properties than either material alone.
3) For example, you can reinforce plastic with glass fibres or carbon fibres to make a composite that's much stronger than plastic would be by itself.

Glass-Reinforced Plastic (GRP)

1) Glass-Reinforced Plastic (GRP) is a popular choice for large structural items such as some car bodies and boats.
2) GRP is made from glass fibres bonded with polyester resin. Like plastic, it's light and can be moulded, but the glass fibres make it stronger.
3) The glass fibre is available as woven fabric, matting and loose strands.

Carbon Fibre Reinforced Plastic

1) This is similar to GRP, but instead of glass fibres, carbon fibres are used.
2) Carbon-fibre reinforced plastic is even lighter, stronger and tougher than GRP — but it's more expensive.
3) Products made from carbon-fibre composites include protective helmets, racing cars and bulletproof vests.

'Smart' Materials React to Their Environment

Smart materials are materials that change their properties when their environment changes.

Nitinol

1) Nitinol is a shape memory alloy.
2) It can be easily shaped when cool, but returns to a 'remembered' shape when heated above a certain temperature.
3) So if your glasses are made of nitinol and you accidentally bend them, you can just pop them into a bowl of hot water and they'll jump back into shape.

Percy wished his glasses were made of nitinol.

Thermochromic Ink

1) Thermochromic inks and pigments are used in colour changing products — they react to temperature.
2) When the temperature changes, the product changes colour. The colour changes back when the temperature goes back to normal.
3) They are used in things like babies' feeding spoons so the parent knows the food isn't too hot.

Smart materials, eh — back in my day...

Polymorph is another really good smart material. It's a type of plastic that becomes mouldable at 60 °C. So if you've made a polymorph giraffe and got bored with it, just warm it up and make it into a gorilla.

Composites and New Materials

Nanomaterials are made from nanoparticles — which are really really really really tiny lumps of material — so tiny that you could fit about a thousand of them into the width of one of these hairs.

Nanomaterials Have Useful Properties

Nanoparticles of a material often have different properties from the 'normal' material — that's why nanomaterials can be very useful. They're used to make products such as:

1) Self-cleaning glass for windows — the glass has a coating of nanoparticles that cause dirt to break down so it can be easily washed off by rainwater.
2) Anti-bacterial coatings, e.g. for toys — surfaces can be coated with a nanomaterial which contains nanoparticles that kill bacteria.

Nanomaterials can also be combined with other materials to make a nanocomposite with a very desirable combination of properties. For example, carbon nanotubes have been added to carbon fibre to make bike frames that are very light but still strong. However, a lot of these materials are expensive.

Some People are Worried Though...

Some people are worried that nanotechnology might have long-term risks — but because it's so new there's no good evidence either way.

1) Nanoparticles could be harmful to the environment — because they're really, really small and lightweight, they could be carried into the atmosphere or contaminate water sources.
2) This could make it difficult and expensive to dispose of nanomaterials safely.

Practice Questions

1) What is a composite material?
2) One example of a composite is carbon fibre reinforced plastic.
   a) What improved properties does carbon fibre reinforced plastic have compared to plastic alone?
   b) Give two uses of carbon fibre.
3) Give another example of a composite and suggest two uses for it.
4) Nitinol is a 'smart' material.
   a) What is a 'smart' material?
   b) What special property does nitinol have?
   c) Suggest one use of nitinol.
   d) Give another example of a 'smart' material.
5) What is a nanomaterial?
6) Bill has designed a new toy. Suggest how he might have used a nanomaterial in his design to make the product safer for children.

7) Give an example of how a product could be improved by using a nanocomposite.
8) Why are some people worried about the environmental consequences of using nanomaterials?

Fixtures and Fittings

It's not just materials you need to know about — here are some lovely components to get your teeth into.

There Are Four Main Types of Hinge

Hinges are available in steel, brass and nylon, and can be coated to match a piece of furniture. The part of the hinge that moves is called the knuckle.

1) Tee hinges are often used outside for things like shed doors or garden gates. The longer 'strap' allows the hinge to support a greater weight.
2) They're often covered in black enamel.

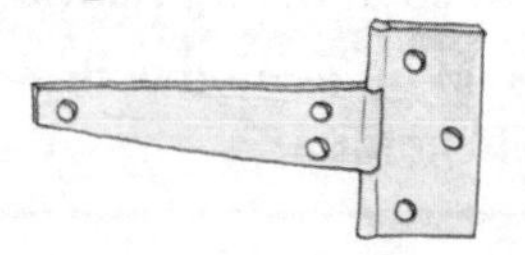

1) Butt hinges are the most common type of hinge used for doors.
2) One part of the hinge is set into the door and the other part is set into the frame.
3) They're available in brass or steel.

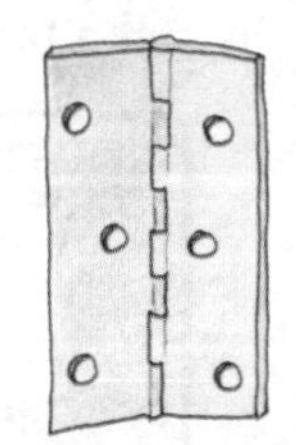

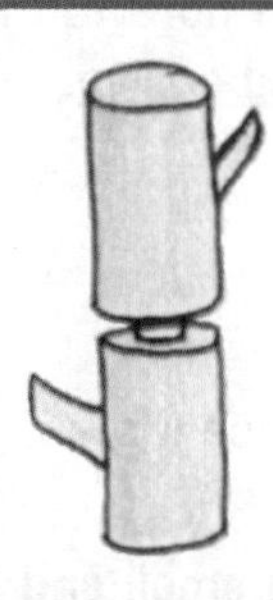

1) Pivot hinges allow you to lift a door off its frame.
2) The hinge is made from two parts that fit together. One part is screwed to the door and the other is screwed to the door frame.

1) Flush hinges are screwed directly onto the surface of the wood, so they're easier to fit than butt hinges.
2) They're usually used for lightweight jobs.

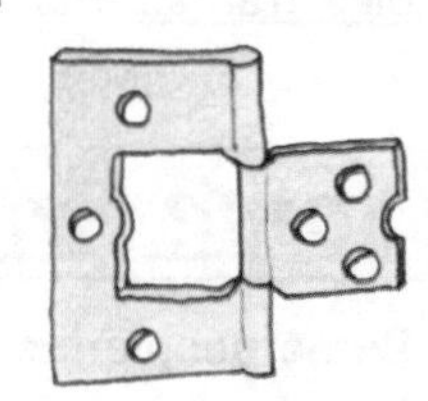

Most Catches and Locks are Made from Steel or Brass

CATCHES

Catches hold a door closed without locking.

1) There are various types of catches available. Here are a few.
2) They can be made out of brass, steel and various plastics.

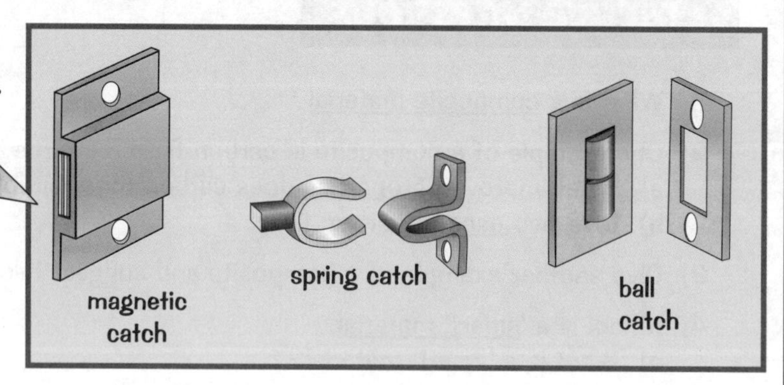

LOCKS

Locks need to be strong so they tend to be made from steel, plated steel or brass.

1) Cupboard locks are screwed to the inside edge of cupboard doors. Turning the key moves the bar out.
2) No cutting is required when fitting the lock.

Learn this page so the exam doesn't catch you out...

This stuff shouldn't be too tricky — 4 types of hinge, some locks and catches, and then some fitments and fastenings to finish with. As long as you know what they're all used for, you're on to a winner.

Fixtures and Fittings

Other Fixtures & Fittings Join Things Together

Some fixtures and fittings can be used to fit shelves or fasten legs onto tables and chairs.

SHELVING FITMENTS

Many shelving units are designed so that you can easily resposition the shelves.

1) The upright part of the unit has holes drilled in it at, say, 5 cm intervals.
2) You just push the fitments into the holes then place the shelf onto the fitments.
3) You can easily remove the fitments if you want to move the shelf up or down.

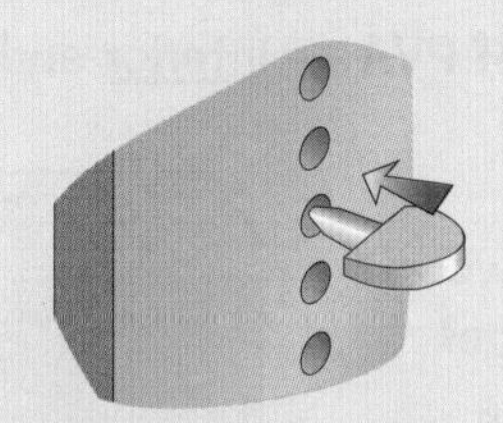

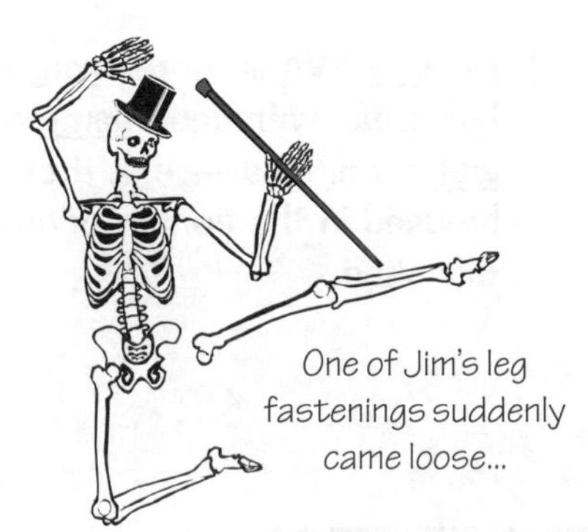

One of Jim's leg fastenings suddenly came loose...

LEG FASTENINGS

You can use leg fastenings to attach legs to tables or chairs. They're useful where the joints may need to be taken apart again — you just have to take out a few screws.

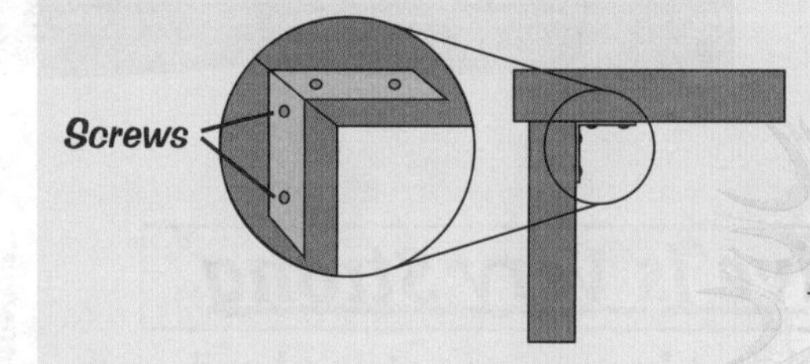

EXAM TIP

Remember, you get marks for naming the components you'd use to make things.

Practice Questions

1) Jack is making a door for a small kitchen cupboard. What type of hinge should he use?
2) Name the two types of hinge below:
   a)

   b)

3) Both butt hinges and pivot hinges can be used for doors. Describe one advantage of using a pivot hinge.
4) Suggest a suitable material for making a lock. Explain your answer.
5) What are catches used for?
6) Colin is making a table using wood.
   a) Make a sketch to show how he could use leg fastenings to attach the legs to the top of the table.
   b) Suggest one advantage of using leg fastenings.

Adhesives

Adhesives are used for joining materials together. The kind you need to use depends on what materials you're joining. It's gripping stuff (geddit?) so seatbelts on, here we go.

Polyvinyl Acetate (PVA) is Used for Wood

1) Polyvinyl acetate (PVA) is a woodworking glue.
2) It's white and creamy and easy to use.
3) There are two types of PVA — interior and exterior.

4) Interior PVA will join wood as long as it doesn't get wet — e.g. it could be used to glue the knobs to a chest of drawers.

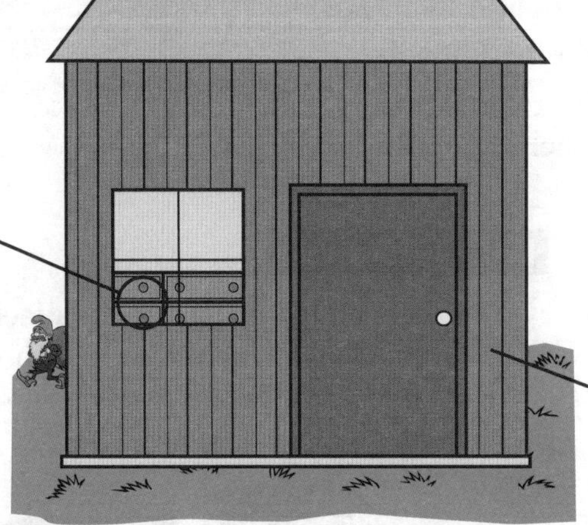

5) Exterior PVA is more expensive but it can withstand damp or wet conditions — e.g. it could be used in the construction of this shed.

Contact Adhesive is Very Strong

1) This glue is rubber based, and forms a very strong bond.
2) It can be used for most household materials — it's particularly useful for sticking down things like floor tiles.
3) You apply it to both surfaces and then keep the surfaces apart until the glue goes tacky.
4) Then when the surfaces are brought into contact, the sticking is pretty instant.
5) Contact adhesive gives off harmful fumes — so make sure the area is well-ventilated.

Floor tile lying upside down while the glue goes tacky

Epoxy Resin Sticks Almost Anything

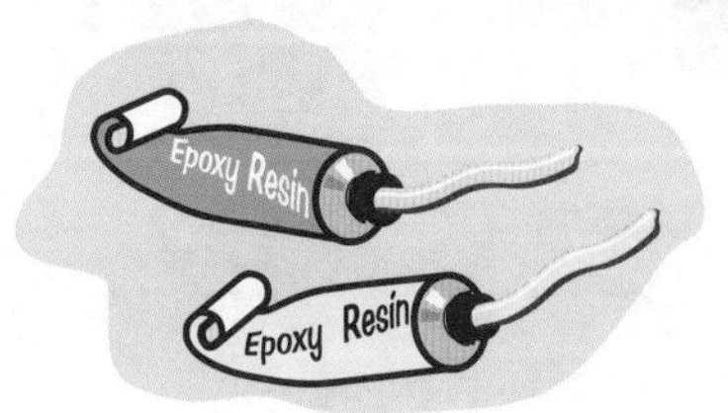

1) A common type of epoxy resin is Araldite®.
2) Two separate substances are mixed in equal parts — they're both thick, sticky liquids, but one is yellow and one is clear.
3) Once the liquids are mixed, epoxy resin will stick almost anything — ceramic to ceramic, metal to wood, wood to plastic, etc.
4) It takes about 15 minutes to harden.
5) The downside is that it's expensive.

Adhesives — should stick in your head pretty easily...

You've made it through to the last two pages of the section. Just five types of glue to learn, then you can give yourself a well-earned pat on the back. But not if you've got superglue on your hand.

Adhesives

Nearly there. Just another two to go...

Superglue Also Sticks Most Things

Simon instantly regretted not removing the superglue from his fingers.

1) Superglue is even more expensive than epoxy resin.
2) However, it'll stick to most things.
3) It certainly sticks to skin, so you have to be very careful.
4) It's a thin, clear liquid.
5) After applying the glue, slight pressure is required for a very strong bond.

Acrylic Cement is Used for Plastics

1) A common type of acrylic cement is Tensol®.
2) It's used for joining plastics together.
3) It's also used in orthopaedic surgery, e.g. to stick artificial joints to bones.
4) It's a watery, clear liquid.
5) The two plastic surfaces need to be clamped together for 24 hours so that a permanent bond can form.
6) Like contact adhesive, it gives off harmful fumes — so you need to use it in a well-ventilated place.

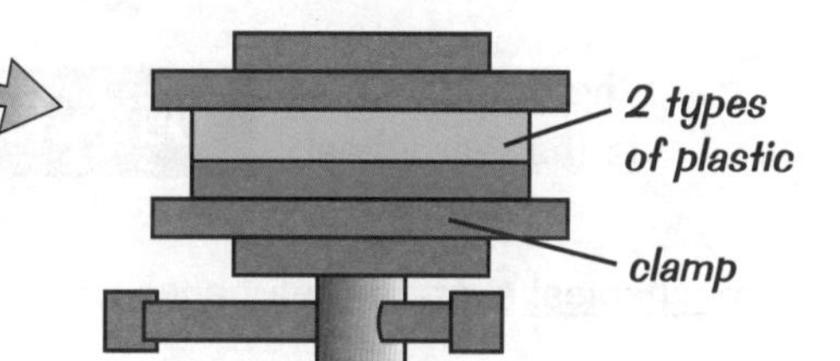

Practice Questions

1) What is PVA glue used for?
2) Suggest a glue that you might use for sticking down carpet tiles.

3) James works for a company that makes model cars. The parts are made from plastic. Suggest a glue that could be used to join the parts together.
4) Sarah wants to stick ceramic tiles to a wooden table top.
   a) Outline how she could use epoxy resin to do this.
   b) Give one problem with using epoxy resin.
5) Katie is making a birdtable for her garden using wood. Suggest a type of glue that she could use to stick the parts together.
6) Ray is assembling a note-pad holder using acrylic cement.
   a) Give one precaution that Ray needs to take when using this type of glue.
   b) Explain why he needs to take this precaution.

Electrical Systems

A system is a collection of parts that work together to do a particular function.
For example, a clock is a system of parts that work together to show the time.

A System has an Input, a Process and an Output

1) A system can be broken down into three 'blocks' — input, process and output.
2) A signal (e.g. electricity or movement) passes from one block to the next.
3) Each block changes the signal in some way.
4) A simple example is a bicycle. In this system the signal starts off as turning motion of your legs and gets changed into forwards motion of the wheels:

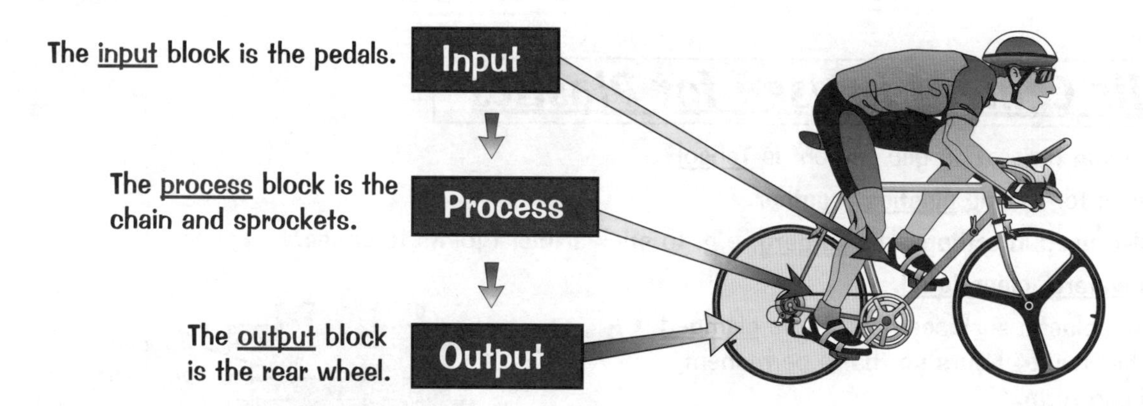

A bike is a mechanical system (see pages 56-61). You need to know about electrical systems too...

Electrical Systems Involve Circuits

1) All electrical systems need to have a complete circuit to make them work. Here's a simple circuit:

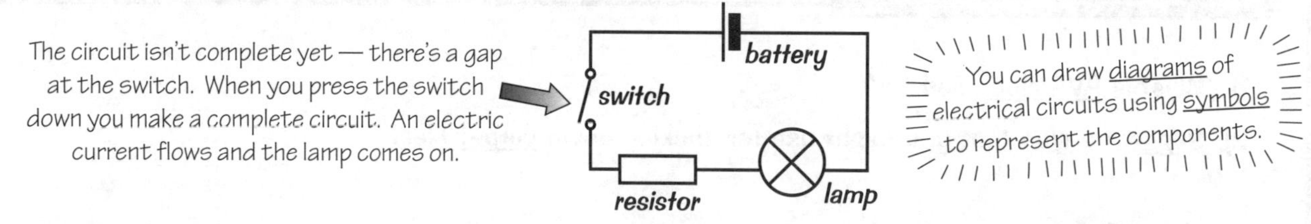

The circuit isn't complete yet — there's a gap at the switch. When you press the switch down you make a complete circuit. An electric current flows and the lamp comes on.
battery
switch
resistor
lamp
You can draw diagrams of electrical circuits using symbols to represent the components.

2) The materials you use in a circuit have to be conductors — they need to let electricity flow through. For example, copper wire is used to join all the components because it's a good conductor.
3) Insulators (e.g. PVC) don't let electricity through, so they're used to coat the outside of wires.
4) Resistors are used to reduce the current in a circuit so you don't damage delicate components.
5) Voltage from a battery or the mains pushes the electric current around a circuit.

- Mains power is used for non-portable products like fridges and televisions.
- Batteries are used in portable products. There are disposable batteries and rechargeable ones.
- Rechargeable batteries are more expensive than disposable batteries, but can be cheaper in the long run as you don't need to keep replacing them. They're built in to some products, e.g. mobile phones.

Watch out for the cake — it's got an electric current...

One system block often contains lots of components. For example, a motor contains loads of different parts but you can still think of it as just a single block in your system (usually it'll be the output).

Electrical Systems

Electrical systems all have input, process and output blocks. But it's not as bad as it sounds — an input block is often just a simple device like a switch, and an output block could just be a bulb.

Input Devices Include Switches and Sensors

There are various input devices you could use in a product.

1) Switches turn a circuit on and off — you can get toggle, push and slide switches.

toggle switch
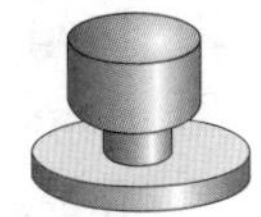
push switch
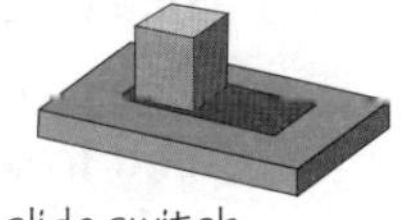
slide switch

2) Light-dependent resistors (LDRs) sense changes in light levels — so that, for example, circuits can be turned on or off when it gets light or dark. Garden lights often use LDRs — the circuit is turned on when it gets dark.
3) Thermistors sense changes in temperature. They're used in central heating systems that turn off when a room reaches a certain temperature.

Process Devices Can Be Complicated

Process devices include timers, amplifiers and pulse generators (used in flashing bike lights). They often involve quite complicated electrical circuits, but you can treat them as a single 'block'.

Output Devices Include Lights, Buzzers and Motors

What output device you use in a system depends on what your product has to do.

1) Lamps (bulbs) and LEDs (light emitting diodes) both give off light. LEDs come in a variety of colours and they don't use much energy. Red LEDs are often used for rear bike lights — because they don't use much energy they don't make the batteries run down quickly.
2) Buzzers make a noise. They're used in alarm clocks, etc.
3) Motors make something move. They're used in, well, loads of things that move.

EXAMPLE — an electronic egg timer

You press a **Switch** which starts a **Timer** which sets off a **Buzzer**

Practice Questions

1) A simple system has three blocks. What are they?
2) a) What material is used to join the components in an electrical circuit?
   b) Explain why this is a suitable material.
3) Voltage from the mains supply can be used to push the electric current around a circuit. What else can provide voltage for a circuit?
4) Calum has designed an outdoor light that comes on when it gets dark. What type of input device might he have used in his circuit?
5) Juan is designing an alert buzzer that will go off when his greenhouse gets above a certain temperature. He decides to use a thermistor as an input device.
   a) What is a thermistor?
   b) What is the output device in this electrical system?

Mechanical Systems

Electrical systems aren't the only type of system. Oh no. There are also mechanical systems.

Mechanisms Change Input Motion into Output Motion

1) All mechanical systems have mechanisms which transform an input motion into an output motion.
2) They're designed so you can gain an advantage from using them — they make something easier to do.
3) Some mechanisms change one type of motion into another.

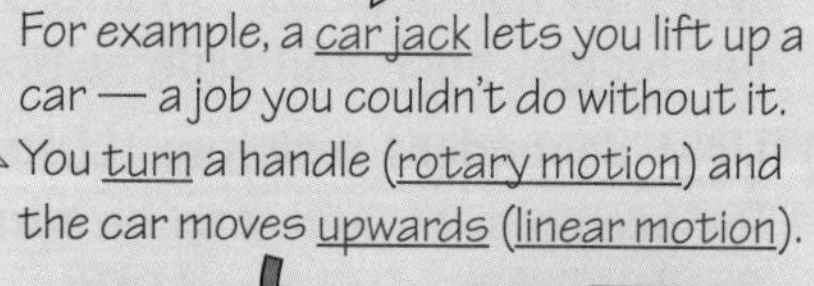

For example, a car jack lets you lift up a car — a job you couldn't do without it. You turn a handle (rotary motion) and the car moves upwards (linear motion).

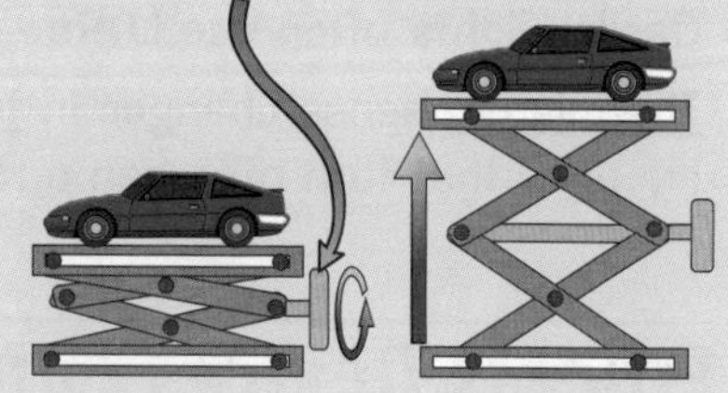

There are various types of motion:

- Linear motion — moving one way in a straight line.
- Reciprocating motion — moving backwards and forwards in a straight line.
- Oscillating motion — moving backwards and forwards in an arc, e.g. a swing.
- Rotary motion — moving in a circle, e.g. a wheel.

Gear Trains Transmit Rotary Motion

Gears are toothed wheels that interlock. A gear train is where two or more gears are linked together.

The driver gear, turned by hand or a motor, turns the driven gear. Both will automatically turn in different directions — if the driver turns clockwise, the driven will turn anticlockwise and vice versa.

If you use a third gear (called an idler), the driver and the driven gears will both turn in the same direction. The size of the idler won't alter the speed of the other two gears.

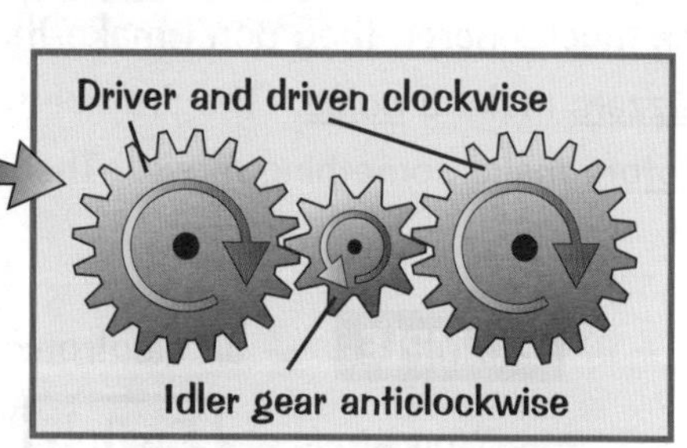

If linked gears are different sizes, they will turn at different speeds. This driven gear has half as many teeth as the driver gear — so it'll turn twice in the time that the driver gear turns once.
(Idler gears have no effect on the speed.)

A compound gear train is where more than one gear is fixed to the same shaft. This is handy because it lets you change the gear ratio easily.

Gears — a topic to get your teeth into...

Make sure you get your head around all the different types of motion before going any further. It might send your head spinning in a rotary motion, but it'll make the rest of this section much easier to learn.

Mechanical Systems

Gears can Change the Type of Motion...

The gears on the previous page all had rotary motion as the input and output. However, you can get gears that can change the type of motion — for example, from rotary motion to linear motion.

RACK AND PINION gears are used to turn rotary motion into linear motion. The pinion, a round gear, is turned to move a flat gear, the rack.

Rack and pinion gears are often used on railways where the track is steep — it stops the steel wheels slipping backwards.

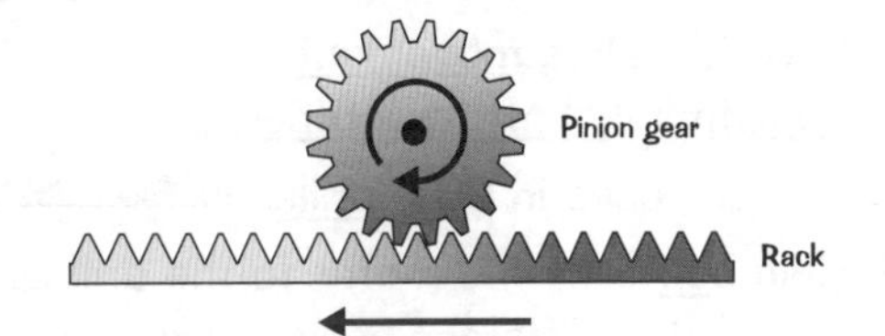

...or the Direction of Motion...

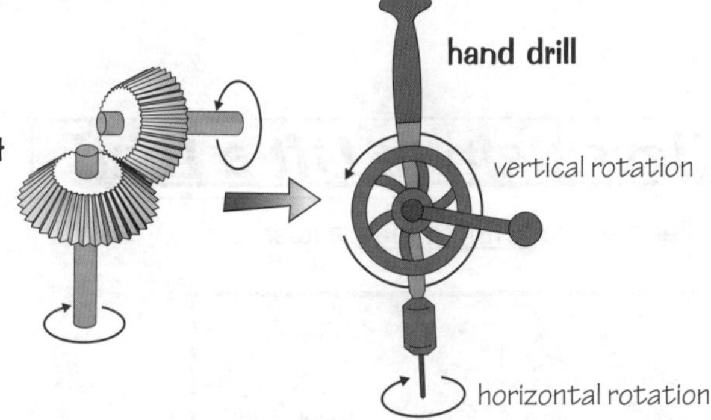

worm drive
This is a bit like a screw. This thread acts as one big 'tooth'.
worm wheel

A **WORM DRIVE AND WORM WHEEL** change the direction of rotation through 90°. The worm drive (the driver) only has one tooth and will turn much faster than the worm wheel, which has many teeth so will turn very slowly.

Worm drives are commonly found in the mechanism used for tightening guitar strings.

BEVEL GEARS also change the direction of rotation through 90°. The teeth are angled at 45° so the gears fit together at right angles.

Bevel gears are used in hand drills — the vertical rotation of the handle is turned into the horizontal rotation of the drill bit.

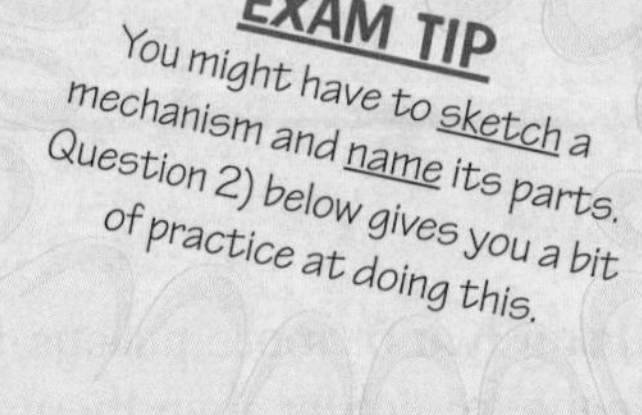

Practice Questions

EXAM TIP
You might have to sketch a mechanism and name its parts. Question 2) below gives you a bit of practice at doing this.

1) What is meant by
   a) reciprocating motion?
   b) oscillating motion?
   c) rotary motion
   d) linear motion
2) Sketch a diagram to show a driver gear turning the driven gear. Label the gears and show the direction that each gear is rotating in.
3) What does an idler gear do?
4) Peter is designing a product which uses a rack and pinion.
   a) What two types of motion does a rack and pinion involve?
   b) Give an example of where this type of gear is used.
5) a) What is the name of the type of gear shown on the right?
   b) Suggest a product in which this type of gear might be used.
   c) This type of gear changes the direction of rotation through 90°. Name another type of gear that does this.

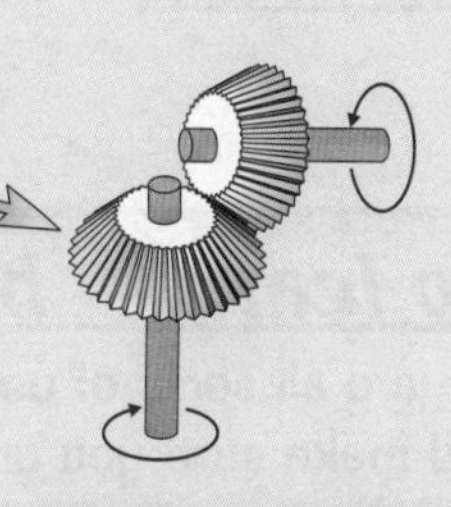

Mechanical Systems

And the fun continues. Remember — mechanisms are great, but they'll eventually stop working if you don't maintain them properly. For example, you have to clean and oil the chain on a bike.

Belt Drives Transfer Movement...

1) A belt drive transfers movement from one rotating shaft to another.
2) Belt drives are used in pillar drills.
3) The flexible belt links the motor to the drill shaft, and can be put in different positions to make the drill turn faster or slower.

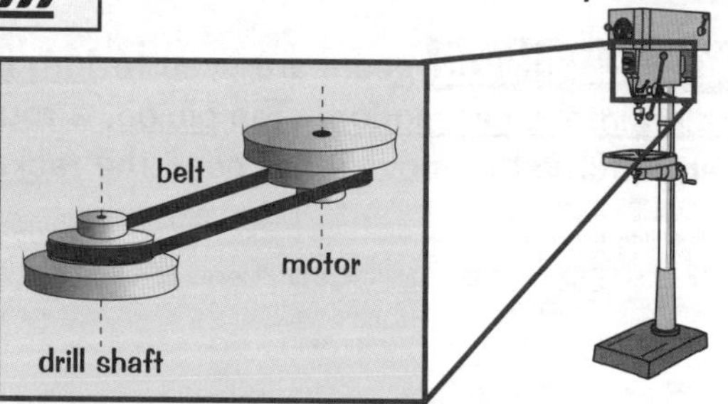

...and so do Chain and Sprocket Mechanisms

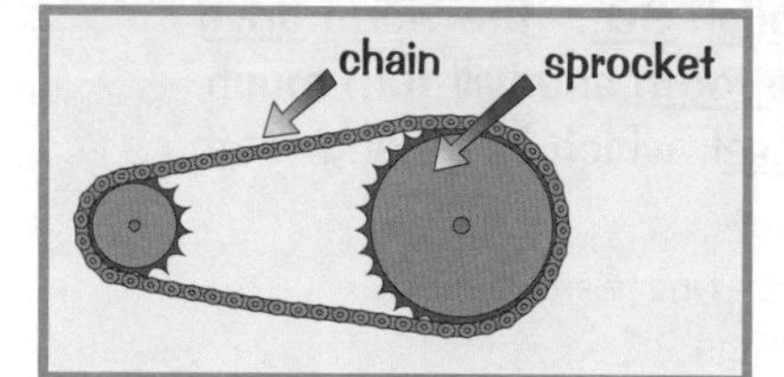

1) A good example of a chain and sprocket mechanism is on a bike.
2) There are two sprockets (toothed wheels) linked with a chain (made up from loads of links).
3) This has the advantage that it can't slip like a belt drive could.

As with gear trains, the size of the sprockets affects their speed.

Pulleys Help to Lift a Load

1) Pulleys make lifting a load easier.

Cranes use pulley mechanisms. Or wings.

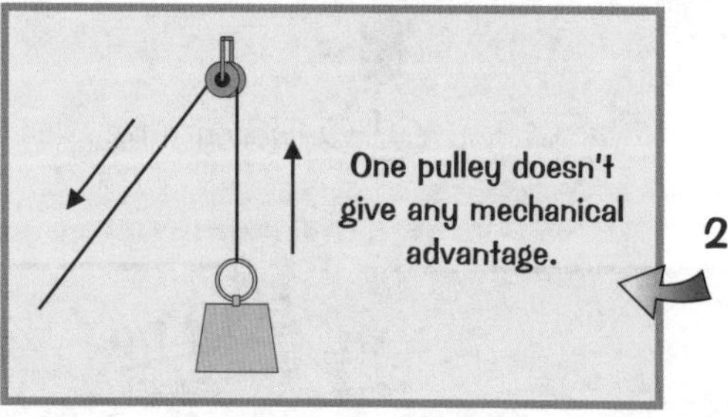

2) One pulley on its own changes the direction of the force required. The same amount of force is needed but pulling down might be easier than lifting something up.

3) Using two or more pulleys together can make things feel a lot lighter than they actually are (if you set them up correctly). For example, one fixed pulley and one moving pulley (a block and tackle) will mean you only need half the force to lift a load.

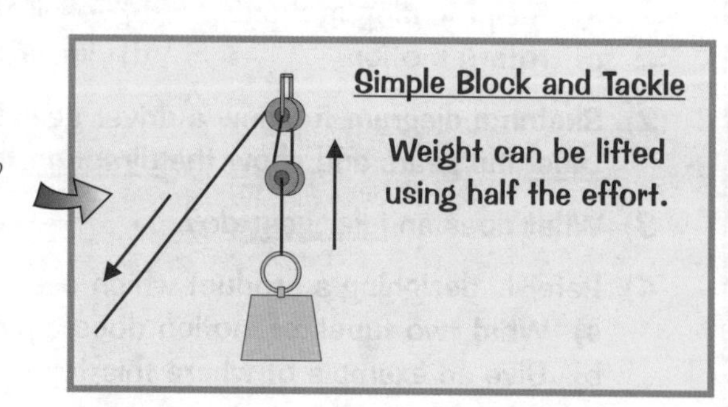

Simple Block and Tackle
Weight can be lifted using half the effort.

Lots to learn — but you cam do it...

Yep, there are all sorts of useful mechanical systems on these pages. But fear not — take them one at a time and make sure you understand what's going on in the diagrams. You'll have it sorted in no time.

Mechanical Systems

Cams Change Rotary Motion to Reciprocating Motion

1) A cam mechanism has two main parts — the cam and the follower.
2) Cams come in many different shapes and sizes. They always rotate.
3) The follower rests on the cam and follows its shape. It may have a small wheel to reduce friction. The follower moves up and down as the cam turns.

Here are a few basic cam shapes:

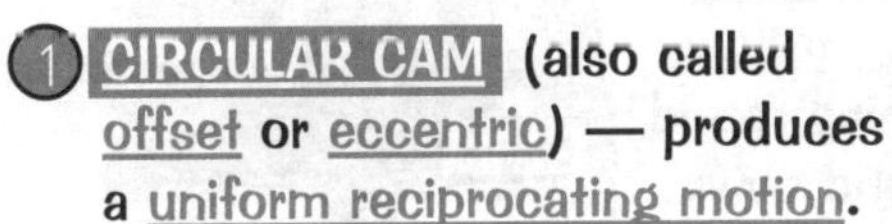

1. **CIRCULAR CAM** (also called offset or eccentric) — produces a uniform reciprocating motion.

The circular cam rotates about an off-centre pivot...

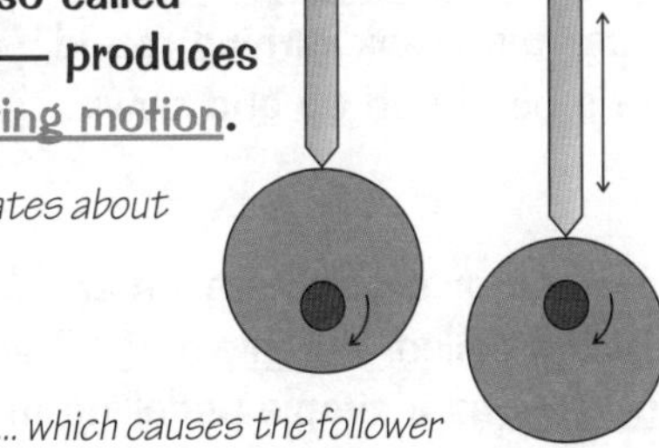

... which causes the follower to move up and down.

2. **SNAIL CAM** — For half a turn the follower will not move, then it will gently rise, and then suddenly drop. It will only work in one direction.

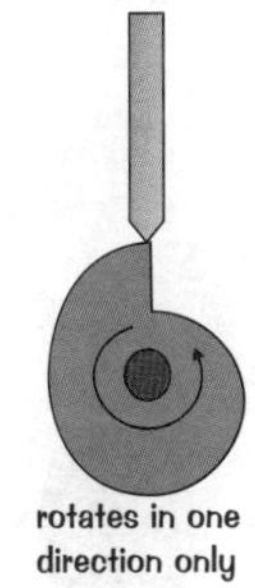

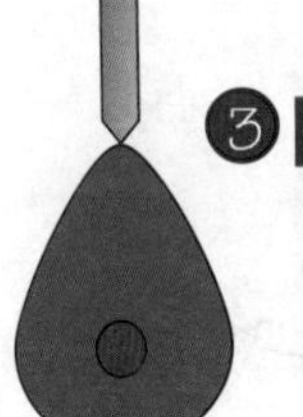

3. **PEAR CAM** — Again for half a turn the follower will not move, then it will gently rise and fall.

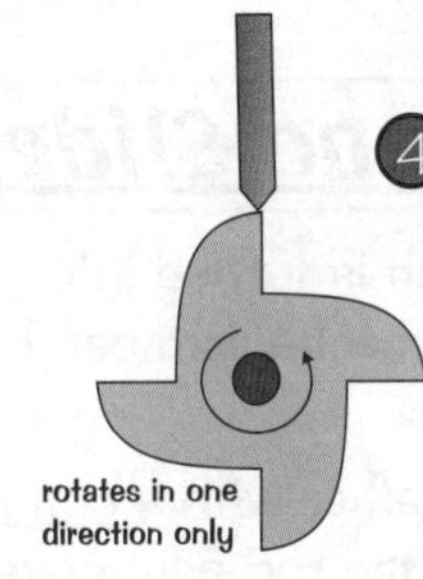

4. **FOUR-LOBED CAM** — Has four lobes (bits that stick out). For each turn of the cam the follower will rise and suddenly fall four times. This cam shape will also only work in one direction.

Practice Questions

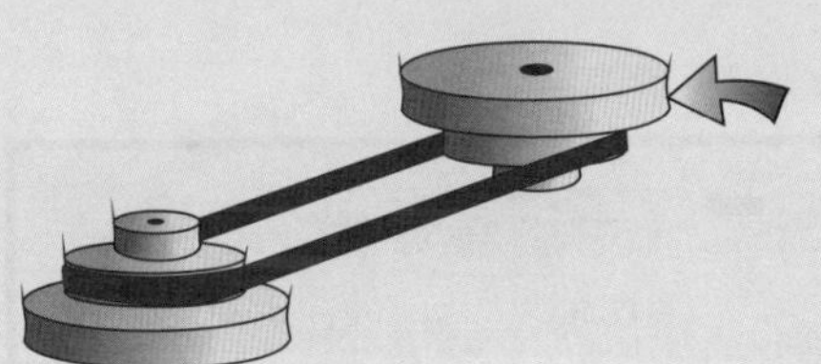

1) a) What is the name of this mechanical system?
   b) Why is this type of system useful?

2) a) Give an example of where you might find a chain and sprocket mechanism.
   b) What affects the speed of a chain and sprocket mechanism?

3) Nadia needs a mechanism that will help her to lift a heavy load of bricks.
   a) Suggest a mechanical system that could help with this.
   b) Explain how it helps.

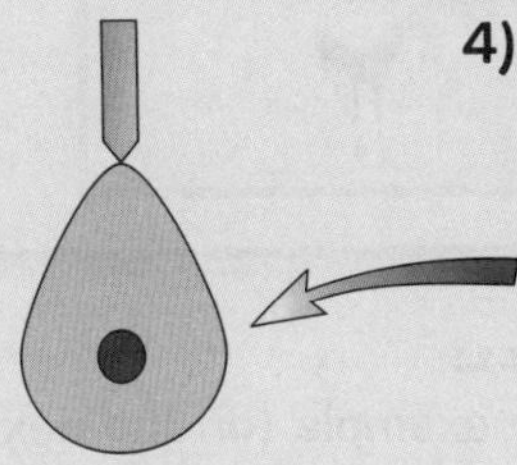

4) Phillip is designing a product which includes a cam.
   a) Describe the change in type of motion caused by a cam.
   b) Why do some cams have a small wheel?
   c) Name the type of cam shown on the left.
   d) Name two other types of cam and sketch what they look like.

Mechanical Systems

The fun's not quite over yet — just cranks, links and levers left...

A Crank is an Arm on a Shaft

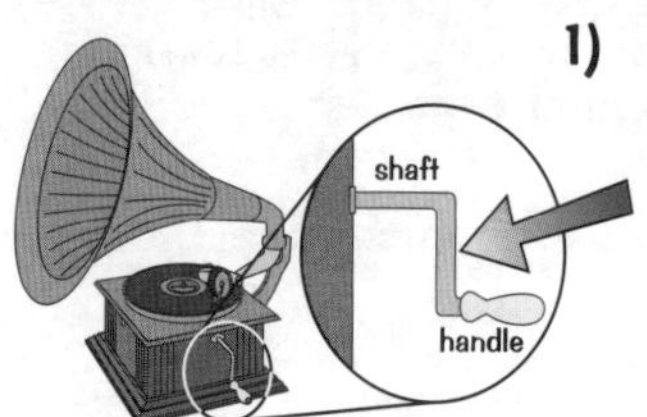

1) A crank can be as simple as an arm on a shaft with a handle to help you turn it (or a pedal, as on a bike). The longer the arm of the mechanism is (between the handle and the shaft) the easier it is to turn the handle.

2) Cranks can be used with connecting rods to turn rotation into reciprocating motion. E.g. in this toy car the crank turning round makes the driver's head bob up and down.

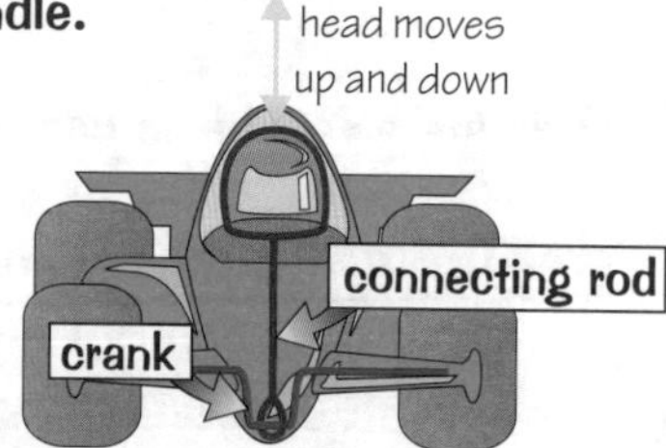

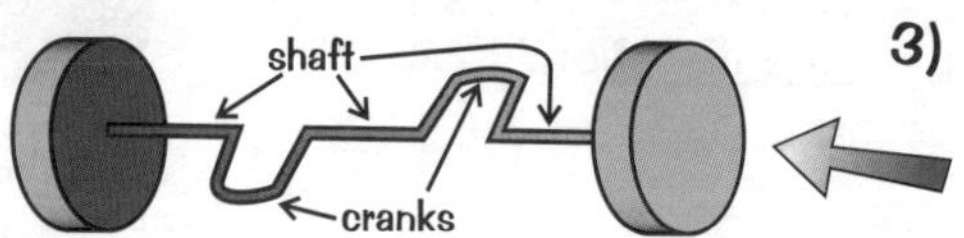

3) When a crank or several cranks are directly on the shaft it's called a crankshaft. They're used on kids' go-karts as a simple pedalling mechanism.

Pistons Use a Crank and Slider Mechanism

1) The up and down motion of a piston is turned into rotary motion by a crank and slider mechanism. This mechanism can be found in the petrol or diesel engines used in most cars.
2) The crank and slider are joined together with a connecting rod. The mechanism won't work unless the rod can move at both ends.

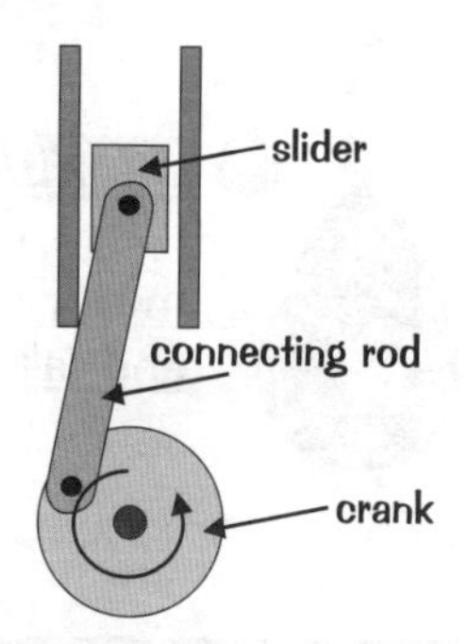

Links Connect Different Parts of a Mechanism

Simple links can transfer forces and change the direction of motion.
Here are a few examples of links:

In this example the input and output motions are in opposite directions.

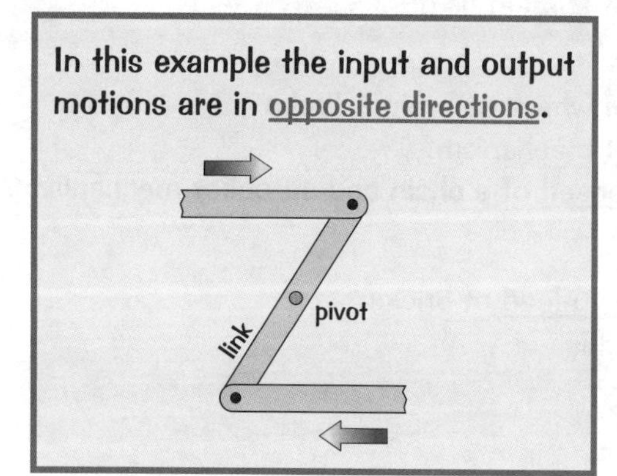

A bell crank changes the direction of a force through 90°.

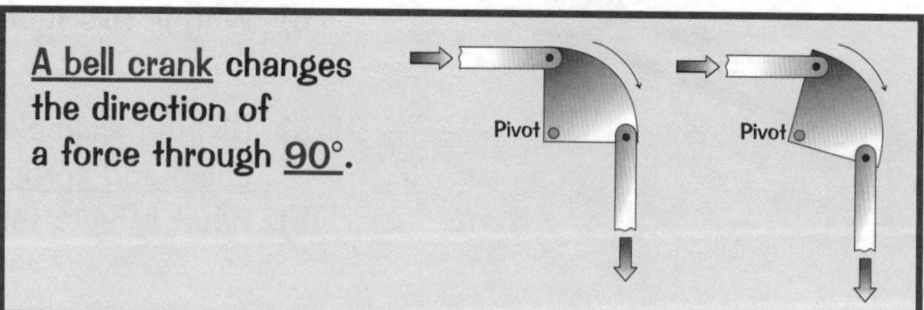

Lazy tongs use loads of levers (see next page) linked together.

Yeah, I'd be cranky too if I had to learn all this...

A lot of these mechanical systems make it easier to do things. Take levers for example (on the next page) — they make it easier to lift a load. If only there was a mechanism to make revision easier...

Mechanical Systems

Levers are used to give a mechanical advantage — to make it easier to move or lift things.

First Class Levers Have a Pivot in the Middle

1) All first class levers have the pivot between the effort and the load.
2) A large load can be lifted using a smaller effort — the lever gives you a mechanical advantage.
3) As you move the pivot closer to the load it becomes easier to lift.

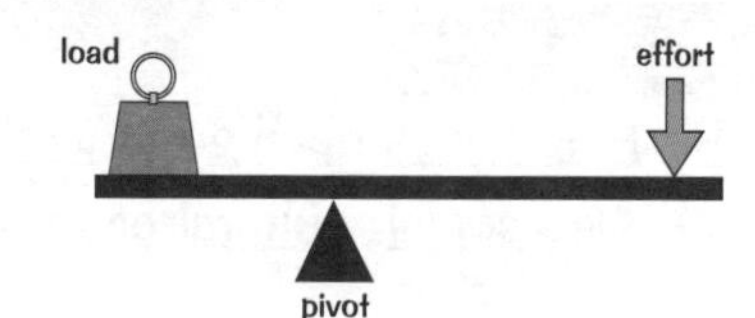

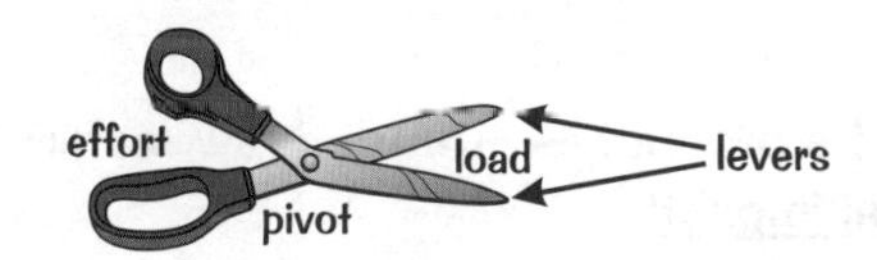

Sometimes levers can be joined together. A double-acting lever is when you have two first class levers hinged together at the pivot point. An example of this is a pair of scissors.

Second Class Levers Have a Load in the Middle

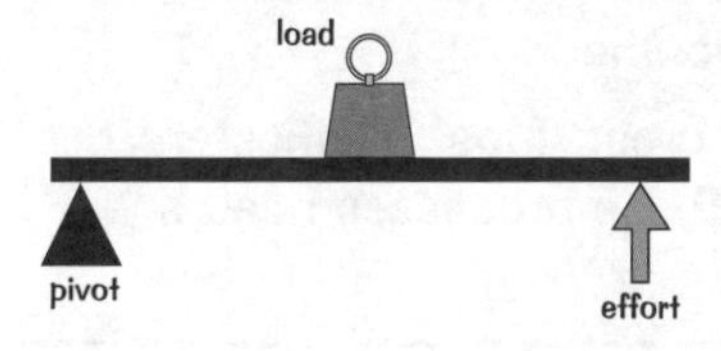

1) Here the pivot is at one end of the lever and the effort is at the other end. The classic example is a wheelbarrow.
2) The closer together the pivot and load are, the easier it is to lift.

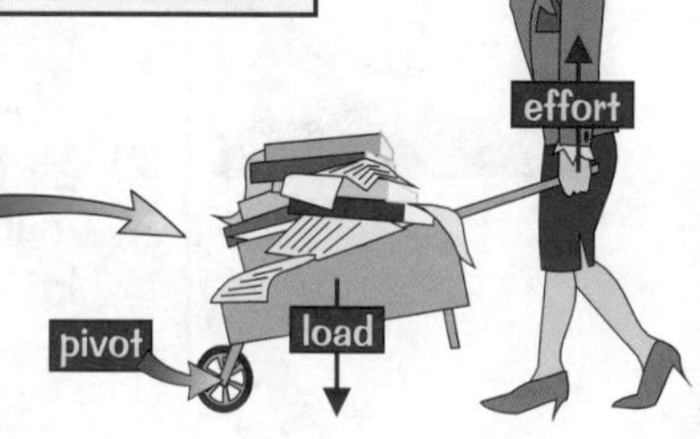

Third Class Levers — Effort in the Middle

1) In a third class lever the effort is in between the load and the pivot.
2) Third class levers can be things like fishing rods, cricket bats and garden spades.
3) Moving the effort and pivot further apart makes it easier to move or lift the load.

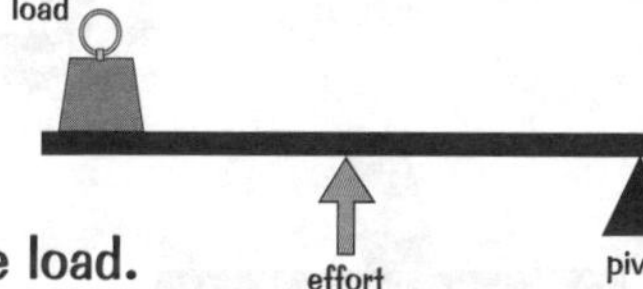

Practice Questions

1) Name two products in which cranks are used and sketch how the crank works.
2) The diagram shows a piston. Draw a sketch to show the position of the slider when the connecting rod is at the top of the crank.

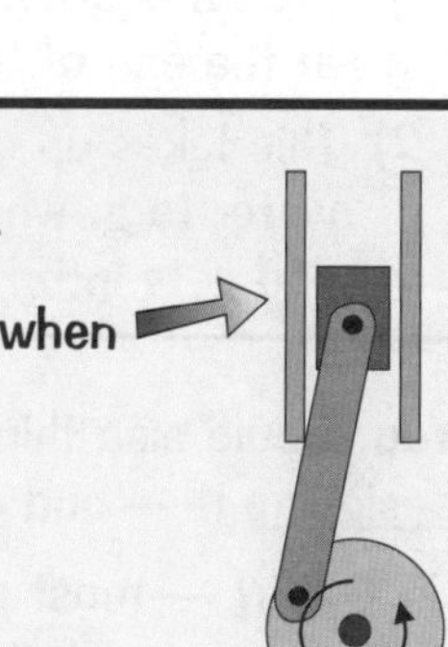

3) Jason has designed a product that uses a bell crank. Draw a sketch to show how a bell crank changes the direction of a force.
4) Hazleen is deciding which type of lever to use.
   a) What is the difference between a first class lever and a second class lever?
   b) Draw a sketch to show how a third class lever works.

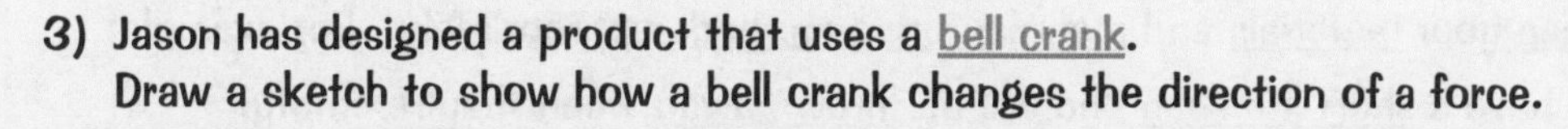

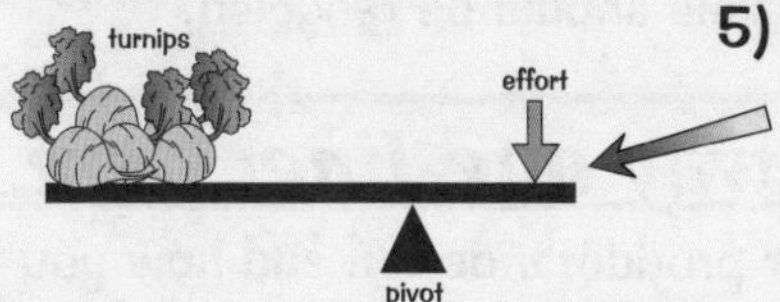

5) Alistair is trying to lift a heavy load of turnips. He sets up the lever shown to the left.
   a) Suggest what he could change to make lifting the load easier.
   b) What type of lever is this — first, second or third class?

Social and Environmental Issues

When you're designing a product you need to take human and environmental factors into consideration.

Products Can Have Human and Environmental Costs

Human costs:

1) Employees need good working conditions, e.g. safe machinery, avoiding child labour, etc.
2) Also social, cultural or religious groups may be offended by the product itself e.g. a T-shirt slogan.

Environmental costs:

A life cycle assessment (LCA) looks at each stage of the life of a product — from the raw materials to when it's disposed of. It works out the potential environmental impact:

Choice of material

1) Hardwoods are often obtained from natural rainforests. Felling the trees destroys the habitat of pretty much everything living there (including people). Softwoods are a greener choice. They're usually from managed plantations — so more trees are planted and grow quickly to replace them. Recycled wood is also a good choice for the environment.
2) Metals have to be mined and extracted from their ores. Most plastics are made using crude oil, which is a finite resource. These processes need a lot of energy and cause a lot of pollution.

Manufacture

1) Manufacturing products uses a lot of energy and other resources. It can also cause a lot of pollution.
2) You also need to think about waste material and how to dispose of it.

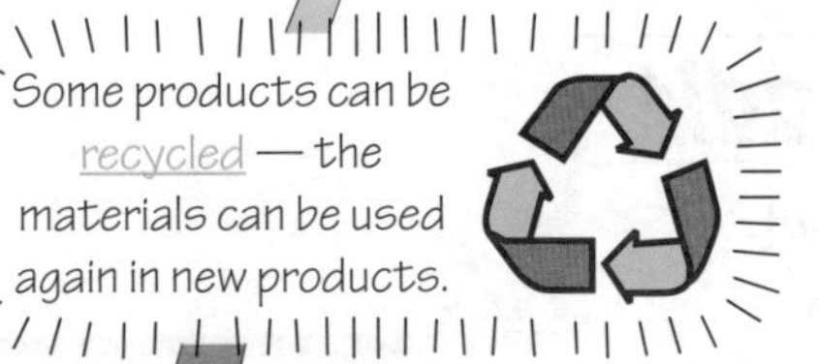

Some products can be recycled — the materials can be used again in new products.

Using the product

Using the product can also damage the environment. E.g. electrical products use electricity generated by burning fossil fuels, and paint gives off toxic fumes.

Product Disposal

1) Products are often disposed of in a landfill site at the end of their life.
2) This takes up space and pollutes land and water (e.g. when paint washes off a product and gets into rivers).

You should also think about a product's life expectancy (how long it needs to last in normal use) when designing it — and choose your materials and manufacturing methods appropriately. For example:

1) A PEN — most pens have a short life span and will be thrown away when they're empty, so cheap materials will be best. They're also designed to have a small number of components so they can be made cheaply and in large numbers.
2) A CAR — cars have a long life span so high quality materials are used that will last. They have a large number of components but these are designed to be easy to replace if they wear out. At the end of a car's life as many parts as possible should be recycled.

Hmm, I could just recycle an old throw-away one-liner here...

This page is all about the importance of thinking carefully about your product's design and how you will manufacture it. It's important to try and minimise any human and environmental costs it might have.

Social and Environmental Issues

Remember to Use the 6 Rs

Something's sustainable if it doesn't use up finite resources or do lasting damage to the environment.

If you consider the 6 Rs when you're designing, you can reduce the impact that products have on the environment and make the whole process more sustainable.

Sonia found a new use for her old toilet brush

1) REPAIR It's better to fix things instead of throwing them away. Manufacturers can still make a profit by selling replacement parts.

2) REUSE Customers can extend a product's life by passing it on or using it again. Some people reuse products for other purposes e.g. using an old car tyre to make a swing.

3) RECYCLE Recycling uses less energy than obtaining new materials, e.g. by extracting metal. Products made from more than one material should ideally be easy to separate into recyclable stuff — clear 'recycle' labelling helps with this.

4) RETHINK You should think about your design carefully — you might be able to make the product in a different way, e.g. a radio that you wind up instead of running off batteries.

EMMELINE WATKINS/
SCIENCE PHOTO LIBRARY

5) REDUCE Making long-lasting, durable products like rechargeable batteries reduces the number of products customers need to buy. It also means that manufacturers can cut down on energy use and transport.

6) REFUSE You can refuse to buy a product if you think it's wasteful — e.g. it might use a lot of unnecessary packaging or be inefficient or costly to run.

Practice Questions

1) Describe two possible human costs of designing and making products.
2) What are the four stages of a life cycle assessment?
3) List the 6 Rs.
4) Bob is designing some disposable plastic cutlery.
   Suggest how he could use the 6 Rs to reduce the impact on the environment.

5) Andy sells sandwiches, and wants to make some boxes for them using cardboard. Suggest some features he could include in his design to minimise its impact on the environment.

Health and Safety

Safety is essential when you make a product — you don't want to lose vital body parts.

Wear the Right Clothing and Protective Equipment

You should always wear appropriate protective clothing (called Personal Protective Equipment — PPE). It's the responsibility of your employer (or school) to provide and maintain this equipment.

If you're working with hazardous materials wear a face mask or goggles and strong protective gloves. If there are fumes make sure there's enough ventilation.
(A spray booth can be used to help remove fumes when using spray glue or paint.)

If the material is hot, you need to wear protective gloves and an apron. For some jobs (e.g. welding metal) you should also wear a face shield.

If you're making a lot of dust you should wear goggles and a face mask and check ventilation.

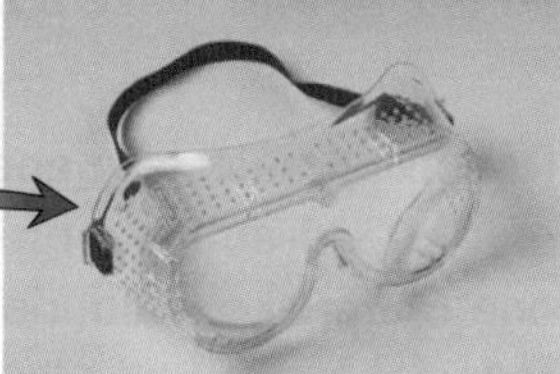

When making large metal castings, you should wear a thick all-body suit, a face shield, gauntlets (thick gloves) and spats (to protect legs and feet).

Be Careful with Tools and Machinery...

1) The Health and Safety at Work Act (1974) was passed to make sure employers provide a safe working environment, and that they use safety signs to help reduce the risk of accidents.
2) When you're working with tools and machinery, make sure you have your sleeves rolled back, ties tucked in or taken off, apron strings tucked in and long hair tied back. Make sure there aren't any tripping hazards in the workshop. Clear up any spillages straight away.
3) By law, employers and workers must always use safe working practices for tools and machinery.

E.g. the pillar drill...

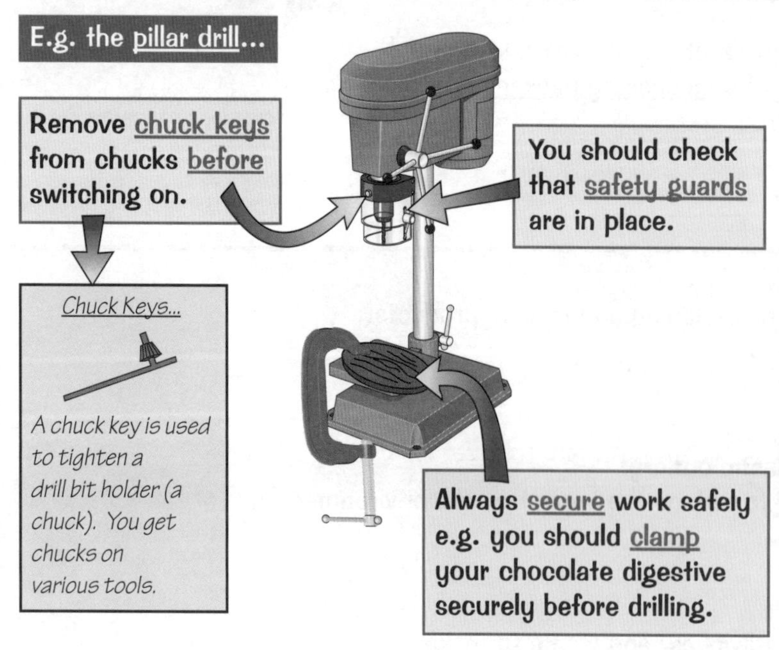

Remove chuck keys from chucks before switching on.
You should check that safety guards are in place.
Chuck Keys...
A chuck key is used to tighten a drill bit holder (a chuck). You get chucks on various tools.
Always secure work safely e.g. you should clamp your chocolate digestive securely before drilling.

Other health and safety procedures

1) Never leave any machines unattended while switched on.
2) Know how to switch off and isolate machines in an emergency.
3) Ensure that any dust extraction equipment is working properly.
4) Never adjust a machine until you've switched it off and isolated it from the mains first.
5) Make sure nobody will distract you or knock you when you're working on the machine.

Watch where you point that tool — nearly had my eye out...

This page is all about minimising risks. Think about clothing, machinery and how to handle materials safely. It's all stuff that comes up when you write a risk assessment (see the next page...)

Health and Safety

...and Handle Materials and Waste Sensibly

1) Choose your materials sensibly — only use hazardous materials where absolutely necessary.
2) Make sure materials are safe to handle. For example, deburr metal (file down any rough edges) before you start work.
3) Be careful when you move long lengths of metal and timber, as it's a possible hazard to others.
4) Beware of naked flames or red-hot heating elements — and keep them away from flammable liquids.
5) Make sure you dispose of waste properly, so that it doesn't harm the environment.
6) Put materials away safely so they can't fall or slide and injure anyone.

COSHH stands for the Control of Substances Hazardous to Health. The COSHH regulations were introduced in 1988 to protect people from the effects of hazardous substances, materials and processes.

You Should Know How to do a Risk Assessment

A risk assessment is when you identify any potential risks of using chemicals, machinery or equipment. Then you can put precautions in place to minimise the risk, e.g. placing warning signs on machines, or erecting barriers and guards.

When you're writing a risk assessment think:
1) What could go wrong?
2) What effect would this have?
3) What can I do to prevent it happening?
4) What precautions could I take to make sure the risk is minimised?

Here's the pillar drill again:

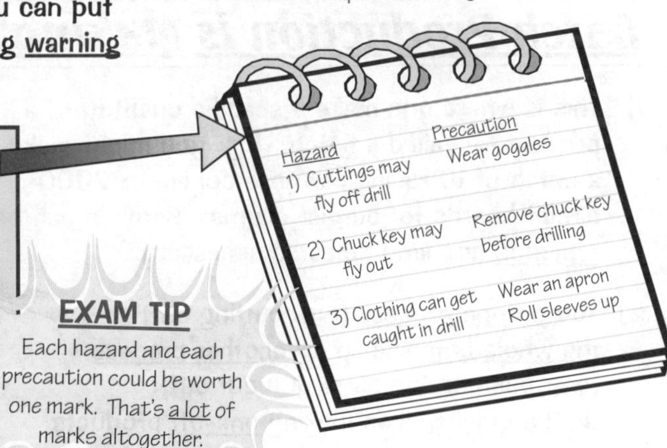

Hazard
Precaution
1) Cuttings may fly off drill
Wear goggles
2) Chuck key may fly out
Remove chuck key before drilling
3) Clothing can get caught in drill
Wear an apron
Roll sleeves up

EXAM TIP
Each hazard and each precaution could be worth one mark. That's a lot of marks altogether.

Practice Questions

1) What protective equipment should you wear if you are:
   a) working with toxic chemicals?
   b) welding metal?
   c) making a lot of dust while sanding?
   d) casting metal?
2) List four health and safety procedures that should be followed when using tools and machinery.

3) What does COSHH stand for? Why do the COSHH regulations matter?
4) Barry needs to carry out a risk assessment for operating a bench grinder. Make a list of hazards and precautions.

Scale of Production

Small scale production means making a few of something. Large scale production could mean making millions. Different scales of production mean different ways of organising things.

Jobbing Production is making a One-off Product

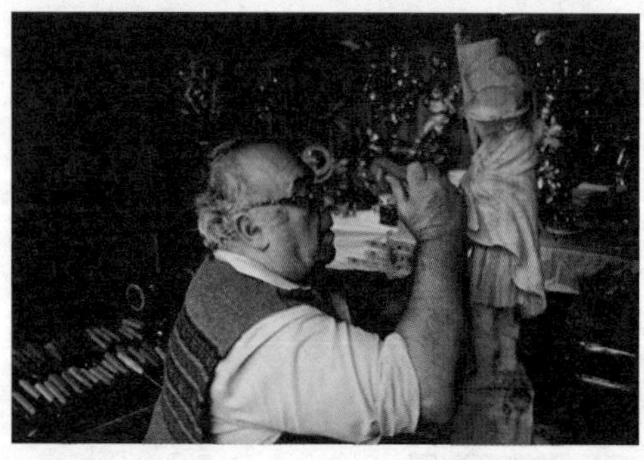

1) This is where you make "one-of-a-kind" products. Every item will be different, to meet a customer's exact requirements.
2) This type of production is very labour intensive — it takes a lot of time to make each product. The workforce also needs to be highly skilled. So it's an expensive way to make things.
3) One-off production is used for all sorts of things, from made-to-measure furniture to buildings like Wembley Stadium.

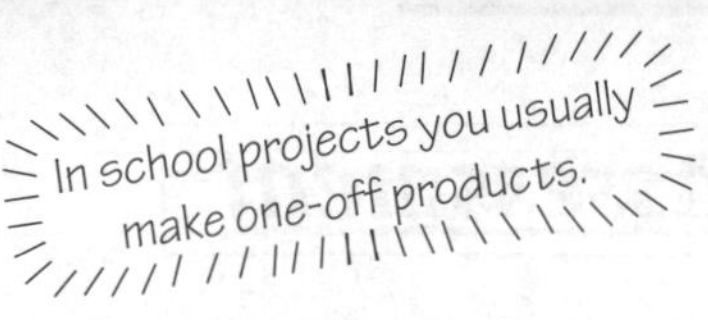

In school projects you usually
make one-off products.

Batch Production is Making a Set Number of Products

1) This is where you make a specific quantity of a product — called a batch. E.g. you might make a batch of 10 racing car nose cones, or 2000 circuit boards for burglar alarms. Batches can be repeated as many times as necessary.
2) You do one process (e.g. cutting out) on the whole batch, then do another process (e.g. painting the parts you cut out). So it's quicker than making one-off products over and over again.

3) Batch production is used to manufacture a load of one product (sofas, say) — then a load of something a bit different (armchairs, for example).
4) The machinery and labour need to be flexible, so they can quickly change from making one batch to making another batch of a similar product.
5) The time between batches, when machines and tools may have to be set up differently or changed, is called down time. This wastes money — because you're not making anything to sell.
6) Batch production could also mean you get a backlog of half-made products, waiting for the slowest process (e.g. paint drying). So it's not as efficient as mass production (see the next page).

Trevor could only hope that his colleagues hadn't used the last of the milk.

Der der der der, derder-der der der — it's batch of the day...

In your exam, you might be given an example of a product and asked what method you would use to manufacture it. Avoid exam pain — learn these methods, and the amount of products they make.

Scale of Production

Mass Production is Making Loads of the Same Product

1) This is the method you'd use to make thousands and thousands of identical products, like cars and televisions. You'd only use this for a mass-market product — where loads of people want to buy the same thing.
2) The different stages of production and manufacture are broken down into simple repetitive tasks which people can easily learn. Production often happens on an assembly line — the product moves further down the line for each different stage. Each worker only does a small part of the process.
3) Mass production often uses computer-aided manufacturing and expensive specialised equipment. E.g. you might use vacuum-forming to mould plastic in jobbing or batch production, but injection moulding is better for mass production — although it costs a lot to set up, it's much faster (see p.25).
4) Recruitment is relatively easy — most of your staff don't need to be highly skilled.

Continuous Production is Making Stuff Non-Stop

1) Continuous production is highly automated. It uses expensive machines that run all the time, without interruption, 24 hours a day.
2) That's because it would be too expensive to keep stopping and restarting the process, especially if certain conditions need to be kept constant, e.g. a high temperature in steel production.

3) The equipment is built to make huge amounts of only one thing, so it can be designed to be very efficient. So it's great for making bulk amounts of materials — like steel, sheet glass, or synthetic fibres for cloth or rope.

Practice Questions

1) List the four main production methods in order of scale (from the smallest to largest scale).
2) Why are one-off products usually expensive to buy?
3) a) What type of production would you use to make a specific quantity of a product?
   b) Why, in that production method, do your workers and machinery need to be flexible?
4) What is 'down time'? Why does it reduce efficiency?

5) You've been asked to make 75 000 musical microwave ovens.
   a) What method of production will be best suited to this task?
   b) What is the advantage of this method when it comes to hiring workers?
6) Fred works in a factory that mass-produces cars. Fred only knows how to do the spray painting. Explain why the factory boss doesn't mind that Fred doesn't understand the rest of the process.
7) a) Why is continuous production very efficient?
   b) So why isn't continuous production used to make everything?

Manufacturing in Quantity

If you were making a batch of products, it'd be a right pain to mark each one out with a ruler before doing the cutting. Instead, you could use a template to save time. Jigs and moulds also speed things up.

Templates are Used to Make Repetitive Shapes

1) Templates are very easy to make and simple to use.
2) You can use them to reproduce any number of identical shapes from one original pattern (template). The template is used to draw, scribe or cut round.
3) Templates need to be strong and hard-wearing — so that they can be used repetitively without getting damaged or worn.
4) Afterwards, the components can be checked against the templates for accuracy.

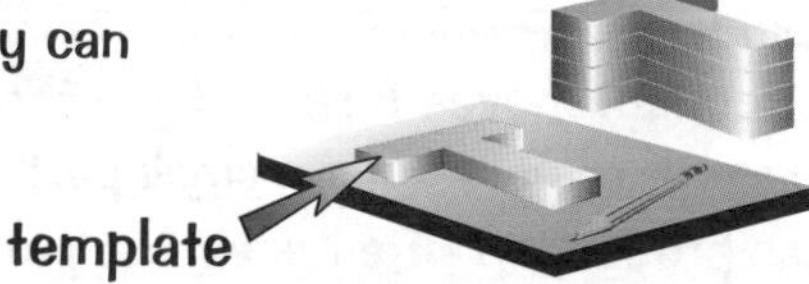

Jigs Help Manufacture Repetitive Components

1) A jig guides the tools that are working on a component.
2) Jigs come in many different shapes and sizes and can be specifically made for a particular job.
3) They're designed to speed up production and simplify the making process.

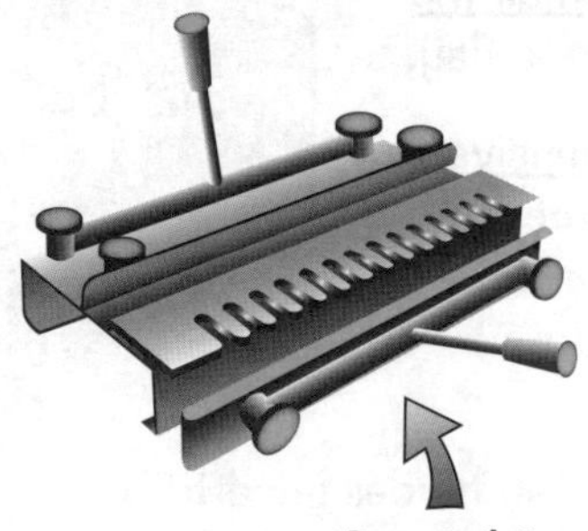
Dovetail jig

4) A drilling jig gets rid of the need for complex marking out. It can also help cut down on errors, and make sure every component is identical.
5) Jigs can help with complex cutting jobs too. E.g. a dovetail jig enables complex joints (see page 30) to be machined with a router, very quickly and easily, and with minimal measuring and marking out.

Moulds are Used to Reproduce 3D Shapes

1) Moulds are most commonly used in plastics manufacturing, in processes such as vacuum forming, compression moulding and blow moulding. See p.24-25 for more on moulding.
2) Once an accurate mould has been made, detailed plastic shapes can be formed with it over and over again.
3) Industrial moulds can be expensive to produce (especially if they're made out of metal), so a manufacturer needs to be certain of the design. It's only cost-effective to make a mould if large numbers of a product are needed.

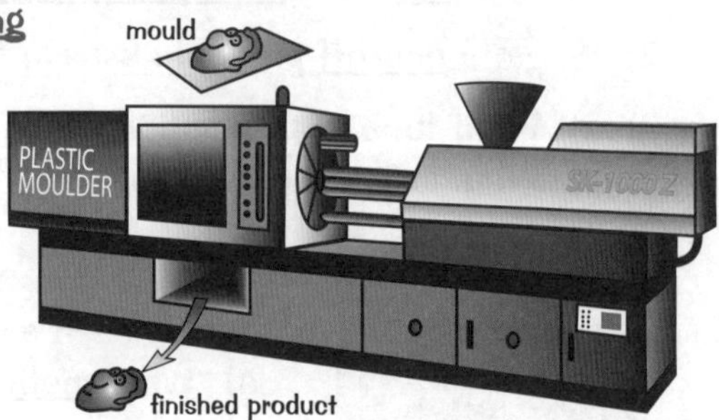

No — there's nothing on this page about Scottish dancing...

This stuff really is worth knowing about. A popular exam question is "Explain how to make a batch of..." That's your cue to show off your template and jig knowledge — so it'd be a shame if you couldn't.

Manufacturing in Quantity

Mass Production is Expensive to Start Up...

Going into mass production means you'll need to fork out for all these things:

1) New technology

To make things quickly and efficiently, you'll need to buy and maintain new machinery.

2) Staff

You'll need employees to make all this stuff or to maintain the new machinery. They'll probably all want to be paid (cheeky so-and-sos).

3) Transport

If you're selling stuff far and wide, you'll need vehicles to transport it. You'll have to pay for loads of fuel too.

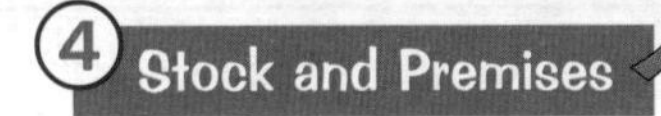

4) Stock and Premises

You'll need to spend money on bigger buildings to put the extra materials and machines in.

5) Organisation

With a big operation you need to plan things carefully — or you risk wasting time and materials. So you'll need managers (who'll also want to be paid).

...But Then Making Each Product is Cheaper

Mass production's cheaper (per product) than small-scale production because:

1) You can make each product more quickly. This saves on wages.
2) Bigger machines are usually more efficient, so they're cheaper to run.
3) You can get discounts from your suppliers if you buy materials in bulk.
4) But — it's a bigger risk. It'll cost a lot to set up, and this money will be wasted if you don't sell enough products.

Time is money...

Practice Questions

1) What are templates used for?
2) a) Give an example of something a jig can help you to do.
   b) Explain why using a jig saves time.
3) You've recently set up a company that makes plastic masks using hand-made moulds. You want to move into larger-scale production using industrial moulds. Explain why you should get some customer feedback on your products before getting industrial moulds made.
4) Your toy-making business is successful. You are receiving large orders from across the world. You are trying to work out if you can afford to mass-produce your toys.
   a) Name five things you have to budget for, and say why you will need them.
   b) You ask the bank manager for a loan. Explain to the bank manager how mass production will make you more efficient.
   c) What might worry the bank manager about this proposal?

Exam Technique

1) The exam lasts 2 hours. There's one paper split into two sections.
2) Section A is the design question. Section B is a load of questions on anything and everything you've learned — tools, materials, processes, safety, etc.

Section A is the Design Question

A bit before the exam, your teacher will give you a preparation sheet. This tells you what the theme of the design question will be. Use this to do some research and practise a few designs.

Design Brief
A company that designs and manufactures children's outdoor play equipment has asked you to design a new slide.

Question 1 is about the design specification.
You are advised to spend about 5 minutes on this question.

1 Analyse the brief above. Evaluate the specific issues that should be considered when designing a slide that is suitable for a child to use.

It should be safe to use — children should not be able to fall off, it should have no sharp edges and finishes must be non-toxic. It should be built to last — the customer won't want to have to replace it after only a short time. The slide should be designed so that it can be manufactured in quantity — this will help to keep the cost down for consumers. Also, it should be ergonomically designed, e.g. the steps shouldn't be too far apart — children should be able to use it comfortably.

(6 marks)

The examiners suggest how long you should spend on each question — pay attention to this so you don't spend too long on a question.

The question asks you to evaluate the issues — so for each one say why it's important.

Think about what issues are really important. The examiners like to hear things like safety, cost and comfort rather than just about a product's looks.

This question is worth 6 marks so make sure you come up with at least three good issues and their explanations.

You are advised to spend about 10 minutes on this question.

2 Study the design brief and your design specification (above). From this information, sketch three different ideas for a slide. Marks will be given for creativity and originality.

(3 × 2 marks)

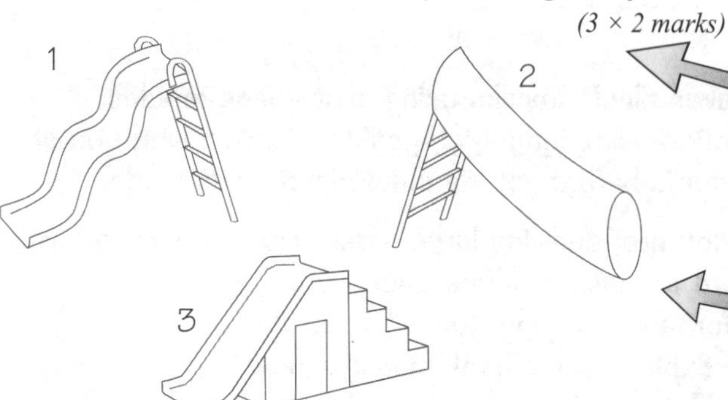

You're just asked to sketch here — your drawings can be freehand and they don't need to be annotated or coloured in. You're getting marks here for how interesting and creative your ideas are.

Make sure you do the right number of sketches — read the question carefully.

Also, make sure each design idea is different from the others — you won't get marks if they're too similar.

Exam Technique

You are advised to spend about 5 minutes on this question.

3 Choose your best design idea.

Best design: 3

Evaluate your best design against your specification.

My design is fairly simple, making it possible to manufacture quickly and in quantity. It is also an ergonomic design — the shallow steps make it easy for children to climb. Also, the curved sides and wide steps make it safe for children to use — they can't fall off when sliding and it is unlikely they will slip when climbing.

(3 marks)

You are advised to spend about 15 minutes on this question.

4 Develop your best design idea using notes and sketches. Think about materials, dimensions and the manufacturing method.

Marks will be given for:

- quality of sketching *(4 marks)*
- quality of notes *(2 marks)*
- specific materials *(3 marks)*
- important sizes *(2 marks)*
- constructional details *(4 marks)*

Slide made from 3 mm aluminium sheet so it won't corrode in the rain. The slide will be attached to the roof of the playhouse with countersunk screws.

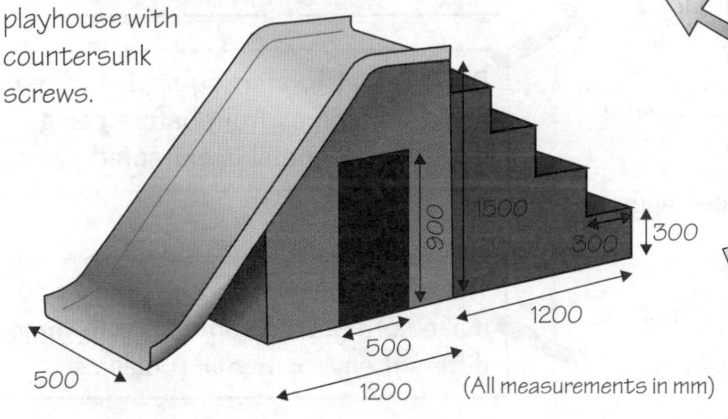

Steps and playhouse made from 25 mm thick marine plywood. This won't rot in the rain.

The wood of the playhouse will be joined with glued halving joints and finished with non-toxic varnish. The wood of the steps will be joined using glued dowel joints and finished with coloured polyurethane paint.

Check you've <u>labelled</u> your sketches <u>correctly</u> — you don't want the examiner looking at the wrong one when they're reading your evaluation.

Make sure you do what the question says and <u>refer back</u> to things that you talked about in your answer to <u>Question 1</u>. The question is worth <u>3 marks</u> — so you need to make <u>three points</u>.

Do your drawing in <u>3D</u> (see p.14 for some techniques) and <u>render</u> it (add shading). Use a <u>ruler</u> for the <u>straight lines</u>.

The examiner is giving you some big hints here — make sure you write or draw something to <u>cover all</u> these points fully.

Say what <u>materials</u> will be used for what parts. Name <u>specific</u> materials, rather than just saying 'wood' or 'metal'.

Give your dimensions in <u>millimetres</u> — you won't get the marks otherwise. You don't need to put every single dimension on — but make sure you put <u>at least two</u> and that they're <u>realistic</u>.

Make sure you say how the product will be <u>put together</u> and <u>finished</u>. Give enough detail for <u>someone else</u> to make the product.

Exam Technique

Here are some of the kinds of questions you'll face in Section B.

Section B Covers Everything

5a Name each tool below, give a process where it would be used and suggest a precaution that should be taken when using it.

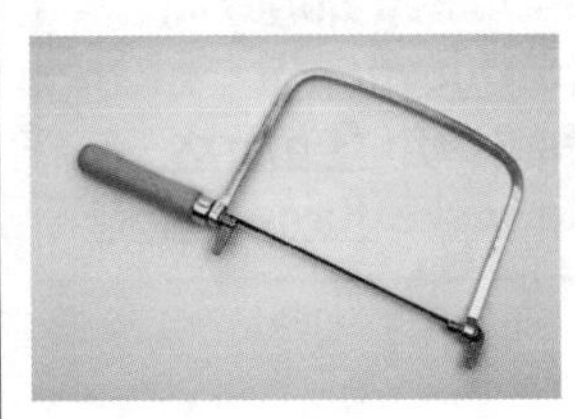

Name: coping saw *(1 mark)*

Process: cutting curves in plastic or wood *(1 mark)*

Precaution: Clamp the material to a work bench so it can't slip while you are sawing. *(1 mark)*

Don't just say saw — say what type of saw it is.

Give a full answer. Rather than just saying 'cutting plastic or wood' the important point to make is that it cuts curves.

Even if you think an answer is too obvious to be what the examiner wants, write it down anyway — some questions will be easier than others. There's no point looking for a more complicated answer.

6a Briefly describe how metal is obtained.

The metal ore is mined from the ground. It is then processed in a blast furnace. This separates the metal from the metal ore. Molten metal from the furnace is poured into casts and cooled. *(2 marks)*

'Briefly describe' means you don't need to go into too much detail, but make sure you've covered each stage. Look to see how many lines there are for your answer and try to fill the space.

Don't forget to start by saying where metal ore comes from before going into how the metal is extracted.

6b Describe the environmental problems associated with using metal ores.

Digging up metal ores damages and disfigures the landscape. Processing the metal ore in a blast furnace uses a lot of energy and causes pollution. Also, transporting the metal ore from the mines in trucks causes a lot of air and noise pollution. *(3 marks)*

The question is worth three marks so make sure you've come up with three different environmental problems.

When you think you've finished, go back and read over your answers to check for mistakes. You might even think of something else you could add.

Exam Technique

7a Look at the design for a letter holder below.

Suggest a suitable, specific material that could be used to make the product. Give a reason for your answer.

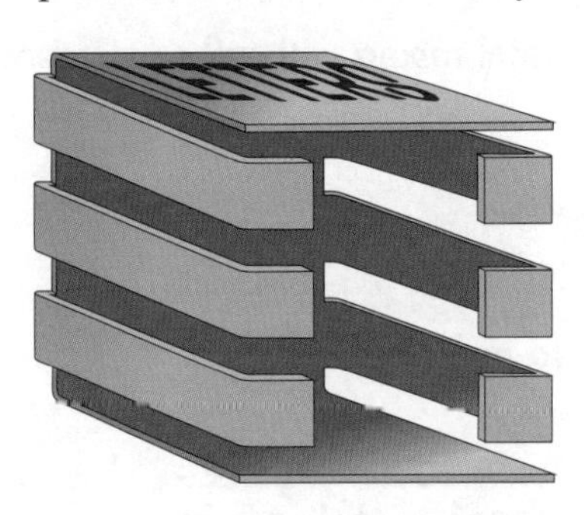

Material acrylic

(2 marks)

Reason It has a smooth finish that looks attractive.

(1 mark)

7b Use notes and sketches to show how you would make a batch of five letter holders in a school workshop.

For each stage, name the tools, equipment and software.

Stage 1: Marking out **or** CAD

Make a template from stiff cardboard of the outline of this shape, using a try square to draw the right angles and a ruler for the lines.

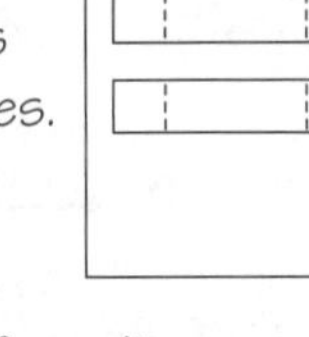

Use a pencil to draw around the template 5 times on a sheet of acrylic.

On each shape, mark lines where the acrylic will be folded, using a ruler to measure the correct distances and a try square to draw at right angles.

(4 marks)

Stage 2: Cutting and shaping **or** CAM

Secure the sheet of acrylic so it can't slip.
Cut out the five outlines marked on the acrylic with a coping saw.
Use a line bender to bend each one into shape.
Allow the plastic to cool so that the heated parts can harden.

(4 marks)

There's always a making question like this in the exam. We've only put a couple of the stages here. The real one will go on to ask things such as how you'd apply a surface finish.

The question asks for a specific material — so don't just put plastic. You'd still get one mark for putting plastic, but you only get both marks for suggesting a specific plastic.

There is usually more than one reason why a material is suitable — but the question is only worth one mark so you only need to put one reason. You won't get any more marks for writing more and it just wastes time.

Do everything that the question asks — make sure you've got notes and sketches, and covered tools and equipment (or software). And note that you're making a batch of five, not just a one-off.

You've been asked to talk about marking out or CAD — don't waste time doing both.

If you did decide to talk about CAD, don't forget to name a suitable piece of software.

Think about what you'd have to do before you start cutting — it's a good idea to think about safety procedures. Then, don't forget to name specific tools — a hacksaw would also be suitable here.

It only makes sense to answer about CAM if you'd talked about CAD in the previous stage. Make sure you name a suitable CAM machine too — a laser cutter would probably be ideal.

Glossary

abrasive	Abrasive materials are used to smooth other surfaces, e.g. sandpaper is used to smooth wood.
alloy	A mixture of two or more metals, or a metal mixed with other elements.
Allen key	One of these
annealing	Softening metal by heating and leaving to cool.
bevel	A bevelled edge is one that's cut at an angle other than 90°. Bevel gears interlock at 45° and turn horizontal rotation into vertical rotation (or vice versa).
brass	A yellowish metal that's an alloy of zinc and copper.
brazing	Joining pieces of metal together using a 'filler' metal such as brass spelter. Stronger than soldering but not as strong as welding.
BSI	British Standards Institution. It sets standards for the quality and safety of products and methods. A product that meets these standards can display the Kitemark.
buffing	Polishing a surface to a shine.
casting	Making a solid object by pouring a molten material into a mould and waiting for it to cool and set.
ceramics	Brittle materials made by heating clay in an oven.
coarse	Coarse materials consist of large particles or have a rough texture.
components	The different parts that are assembled to make a product.
composite	A material made by combining other materials, e.g. glass-reinforced plastic is a composite made from plastic and glass fibres.
conductor	An electrical conductor is a material that allows electricity to flow through it easily, e.g. copper. A thermal conductor is a material that lets heat flow easily.
compression	Squashing something — applying pressure to reduce its size.
corrosion	The 'eating away' of a material by a chemical reaction, e.g. rusting of iron.
deciduous	A deciduous tree loses its leaves in autumn and grows new leaves in spring.
design specification	A list of conditions that a product should meet.
ductile	Ductile materials can be drawn into wires easily.
enamel	Enamel paint dries to a hard, shiny finish.

Glossary

evergreen	A type of tree that keeps its leaves all year round.
finite	A finite resource is one that will run out eventually.
flammable	Something that catches fire easily, e.g. petrol.
flexible	Something that bends a lot without breaking.
granule	A small particle or grain, e.g. plastic can be bought in granules which are then melted for moulding.
hardwood	Hardwood comes from trees with broad leaves (mainly deciduous trees). It is usually denser and harder than softwood.
hazard	A potential danger to humans or the environment.
impurities	Small amounts of other substances within the 'main' substance.
insulator	An electrical insulator is something that does not allow electricity to flow easily, e.g. polythene. A thermal insulator doesn't allow much heat to flow.
landfill	A landfill site is a large rubbish dump that's eventually covered with earth.
linear	Linear motion is when something moves in a straight line in one direction.
malleable	Malleable materials are easy to shape and bend, e.g. thin metal sheets.
mallet	A type of hammer with a large head. Usually made from wood or plastic.
manufacturer's specification	A manufacturer's specification tells the manufacturer exactly how to make a product.
marketing	How companies try to sell their products, e.g. advertising, giving out free samples.
model	A practice version of a product that you make during the development stage. It's probably made from easy-to-work materials and might be scaled down in size.
orthographic projection	A 2D scale drawing of a 3D object showing the front, plan and end views.
oscillating	Oscillating motion is when something moves side-to-side in an arc.
prototype	A full-size, working, one-off model of a design. A prototype is built to allow evaluation of the product before starting manufacturing in quantity.
reciprocating	Reciprocating motion is when something moves backwards and forwards in a straight line.
refining	Making something more pure, e.g. crude oil is refined to make petrol.

Glossary

refinery	A chemical plant where chemicals are processed and refined.
renewable	A renewable resource is one that is replaced by natural processes as fast as it is consumed by humans, e.g. softwood trees in a plantation.
revolution	A single turn of something that is rotating.
risk assessment	Identifying potential hazards and the precautions needed to minimise risks before work starts.
scribing	Scoring a line onto a surface (usually before cutting or folding).
softwood	Softwood comes from trees with needle-like leaves (mainly evergreen trees). It's usually less dense and easier to saw than hardwood.
soldering	Joining two metals together by melting a tin-based alloy between them. Not as strong as brazing or welding.
spelter	An alloy of zinc.
sustainable	A sustainable process or material is one that can be used without causing permanent damage to the environment or using up finite resources, e.g. sustainable wood comes from forests where fast-growing trees are chopped down and replaced.
synthetic	Man-made.
tacky	Slightly sticky.
tapered	Something that gets narrower at one end.
tarnishing	When a metal surface loses its shine and becomes dull. Tarnishing happens because of reactions with the air.
thermoplastics	Plastics that can be melted and remoulded over and over again.
thermosetting	Thermosetting plastics are ones that undergo a chemical change when heated which makes them hard and rigid. They can't be remoulded.
tolerance	How much a component can differ in size from its ideal measurements before the product is affected.
toxic	A toxic substance is one that's harmful to health.
veneer	A thin layer of high quality wood.
warped	When something has changed shape, e.g. untreated wood warps after time.
working drawing	A detailed scale drawing that shows all the dimensions of each part of a product, the materials from which components are to be made, etc.

Answers

Page 3 — Design Briefs

1) a) Market pull is the effect of consumer demand on the design of a product.
   b) E.g. laptop computers
2) a) E.g. what kind of product is needed, how the product will be used, who the product is for.
   b) the client
3) E.g. Make sure the table is big enough to seat a typical large family.
4) a) E.g. computer games — children play outside less, cars — people become less physically active.
   b) E.g. a product with a rude slogan or picture — people may think this isn't appropriate if there are young children around.

Page 5 — Product Analysis

1) It helps you get ideas for a new or improved product.
2) a) Taking a product apart.
   b) It can help you find out how the product works and what materials or components have been used.
3) a) How easy and comfortable a product is to use.
   b) the handle
   c) She should check whether it's comfortable and the right size for the hands of the product's typical user.
4) a) plastic, metal
   b) It might be toxic to children or harmful to the environment.
5) Two from, e.g. whether the process produces pollution / uses a lot of energy / produces a lot of waste / whether conditions are good for workers.

Page 7 — Research and Design Specification

1) To find out about what people like/dislike about existing products. To see if people will want your product.
2) a) The people who are most likely to buy your product.
   b) People who are about to have children.
3) a) E.g. Do you like eggs? Do you already have an egg cup?
   b) E.g. What features would you like to see in an egg cup? How much would you be willing to pay for an egg cup?
   c) E.g. How many boiled eggs did you eat last week? [0], [1], [2], [3 or more]
4) a) A list of conditions that the product must meet.
   b) E.g. colour / material / production method / size / weight / price range.
   c) E.g. must hold two eggs and four slices of toast, should have a shiny surface finish, must be easy to clean, no more than 10 cm tall, must cost less than £2 to manufacture.

Page 9 — Generating Proposals

1) Any three of, e.g. a mood board / brainstorming / looking at an existing product / looking at the work of successful designers / looking at nature / looking at patterns
2) Any suitable ideas.
3) a) E.g. a flower, a leaf, a bird's nest.
   b) & c) Any suitable sketches that meet the specification.

Page 11 — Development

1) E.g. It might help her decide on details of the design.
2) It can be used to model designs in 3D.
3) E.g. cardboard, jellutong, polystyrene foam.
4) E.g. Do you find the chair comfortable? Do you like the look of it? If this product were on the market, would you consider buying it?

Page 13 — Designing Safe Products

1) E.g. a sharp knife — if you made it blunter, it wouldn't do its job.
2) Two from, e.g. make sure they don't have unnecessary sharp corners / make sure the paint or varnish isn't toxic / make sure components are firmly attached.
3) They've already been rigorously tested by the manufacturer.
4) a) Kitemark
   b) It shows that the product meets the British Standards Institution's safety and quality standards.
5) a) The Sale of Goods Act
   b) Fire Safety Regulations
6) The product meets EU standards for safety.
7) Two from, e.g. 'Place on an even surface' / 'Bulb becomes hot during use' / '60W bulb or less' / 'Clean lampshade with a damp cloth'.

Page 15 — Drawing Techniques

1) 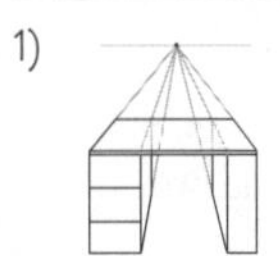

2) Advantage — it's easier to get dimensions right. Disadvantage — it doesn't show things smaller the further away they are.
3) 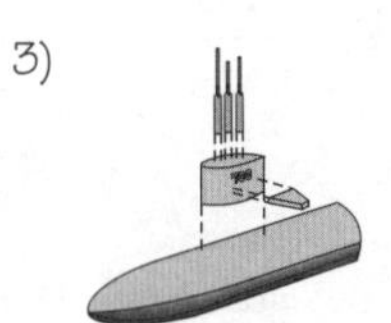

4) E.g. Pro/DESKTOP®
5) a) Centre lines (alternate short/long dashes) and hidden details (short dashes)
   b) millimetres

Page 17 — Planning for Manufacture

1) a) A manufacturer's specification can be a series of written statements, or working drawings and sequence diagrams which explain exactly how to make the product.
   b) Three from, e.g. materials / tolerances / finishing details / costings / quality control checks / sizes
2) Working drawings show the design with the precise dimensions, details of materials, etc., marked on.
3) Put the quality control checks in diamond shaped boxes.
4) a) Some of the processes can happen at the same time, e.g. while the varnish is drying.
   b) 75 minutes
   c) Making the table legs — it takes 25 minutes.

Page 19 — Hand and Power Tools

1) hacksaw
2) cutting curves in wood and plastic
3) bradawl
4) Any two from, e.g. countersink bit — for making holes for screwheads to sit in / flat bit — to drill large flat-bottomed holes / twist bit — for drilling small holes.
5) a) hand tool — bench plane, power tool — planer
   b) The bench plane will be more accurate than the planer.
6) a) E.g. try square — for marking a right angle from the edge of the material, centre punch — to mark where she needs to drill a hole.
   b) 38 mm

Answers

Page 21 — Machine Tools

1) They're more accurate. They can process materials more quickly.
2) Any two from, e.g. tie hair back / wear safety glasses / keep clothes tucked in / know where the emergency stop button is.
3) A circular saw — it's used to cut wood and boards to size.
4) e.g. a planer and thicknesser
5) a milling machine
6) A bench grinder — it can be used to remove metal for shaping/finishing purposes or for sharpening edged tools, e.g. chisels.

Page 23 — Forming and Bending

1) sheet metal folder
2) a) heat it
   b) 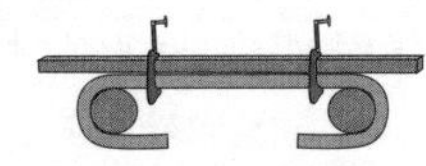
3) (Hot) metals are placed on it to be hammered into shape.
4) a) The strips of wood are glued together and held in a jig, which keeps them bent in the desired shape while the glue dries.
   b) E.g. rocking chair runners, chair/table legs.
5) a) line bending
   b) The element in the line bender heats the plastic along the line where you want to bend it. Once the plastic is soft, it can be bent.

Page 25 — Casting and Moulding

1) a) thermosetting plastics
   b) A 'slug' of thermosetting plastic powder is put into a 'female' mould. A former is pressed onto it and pushes the plastic into the mould. Very high temperatures and pressures liquefy the powder, and the plastic is set into a permanent shape.
2) A sheet of thermoplastic is heated until it goes soft. A (male) mould is put onto the vacuum bed. The bed is then lifted close to the heated plastic. The air is sucked out from under the plastic. This forces the plastic onto the mould.
3) a) blow moulding
   b) 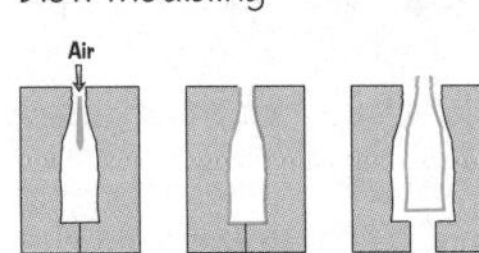

4) a) a mould
   b) metal and thermoplastics
5) a) a plastic
   b) Molten plastic is forced into a closed mould under pressure.
6) E.g. plastic covered wire, plastic/aluminium edgings.

Page 27 — Assembly and Finishing

1) He should double-check the fit of the parts.
2) The joint areas should be cleaned so they're free from dirt or oil. This could stop the joint from working properly.
3) Put it in a clamp.
4) Access to the inner parts might be too difficult once she's assembled it.
5) To make it look attractive. To protect it from rain and dirt.
6) Using a file / emery cloth / glass paper.
7) If you use the wrong paint it might not stick to the material.
8) a) white spirit
   b) metal
   c) It is sprayed on.
   d) As it's sprayed on, a lot of the paint doesn't end up on the product.

Page 29 — Screws, Bolts and Nails

1) a) woodscrews
   b) E.g. round / countersunk / slotted / cross.
   c) To make a pilot/clearance hole.
   d) countersunk
2) a) metals and hard plastics
   b) They cut their own threaded holes.
3) a) nuts and washers
   b) allen key
4) a) bolt
   b) spanner
   c) E.g. steel / brass / stainless steel.
5) a) They're quick to use.
   b) The joint they make isn't very strong.
6) a) Threading is a method of fastening machine screws and bolts directly into a metal or plastic component without using nuts.
   b) A hole is drilled and a tap is used to cut a female thread in the hole. The screw is inserted into it and tightened until it stops.
   c) A split die — for cutting a male thread onto a round rod.

Page 31 — Joints

1) a) lap joint
   b) housing joint
   c) mitred joint
2) They have a large surface area for gluing.
3) They aren't very strong.
4) mortise and tenon joint / dowel joint
5) They are tricky to make.
6) a) Fittings which enable furniture to be assembled and taken apart easily.
   b) E.g. advantage: they're fast to use/they can be taken apart easily, disadvantage: they aren't as strong as glued joints.
   c) (cheap) flat-pack furniture.
7) a) acrylic cement/epoxy resin
   b) They're too smooth / they have a greasy texture which stops the glue from keying in.

Page 33 — Joining Metals

1) soldering
2) tin and other metals
3) a) brass spelter
   b) brazing
   c) E.g. a gas brazing torch / a blow torch / electric arc welder with a brazing attachment.
4) a) The edges of the two metal parts are melted and flow together.
   b) With metal from a welding rod.
   c) Wear a face mask — to protect his eyes and face from sparks and heat / to protect his eyes from UV.
5) So that it's free from dirt or grease. Grease can stop brass spelter from 'taking'.
6) It stops air from oxidising the surface of the metal while you're heating it.
7) a) joining sheet metal
   b) A hole is drilled through both pieces of metal. The rivet is inserted with a set. The head is held against the metal while the other end is flattened and shaped into another head with a hammer.

Answers

c) They can be used where there is only access to one side of the material. / They're quick and easy to use.
d) The rivet and pin are placed in the hole together. The pin is pulled tight with a riveter until it snaps off. This makes the end of the rivet expand, forming a head on the other side.

Page 35 — CAD/CAM

1) Computer Numerical Control
2) a) Additive processes work by adding material to build up the product. Subtractive processes remove material from a larger piece to form the product.
   b) Two from, e.g. milling machine / laser cutter / CNC router.
   c) Two from, e.g. stereolithography / laser-sintering / 3D printing
3) a) It converts a CAD image into a 3D model by printing layers of material.
   b) the development stage
4) Three from, e.g. You can produce accurate shapes and designs on screen / You can easily edit features of the design / Products can be machined quickly / Lots of the product can be made quickly, all exactly the same / Money can be saved on labour costs.

Page 37 — Quality Assurance and Control

1) So that customers are satisfied.
2) An international standard of quality management awarded to companies with good QA and QC procedures.
3) a micrometer
4) 21 mm (± 3)
5) a) yes
   b) no
   c) yes
   d) no
6) They speed up the process of checking whether components are within tolerance.
7) a) To spot defects, e.g. in a welded joint.
   b) He could load weights onto the table until it collapses.
   c) To find out what load the table can carry / how it collapses. This will help the manufacturer to write the safety instructions.

Page 39 — Properties of Materials

1) a) The material won't stretch / is likely to crack or break.
   b) The material can be moulded.
   c) The material can be drawn into wires.
2) a) e.g. a file / drill bit
   b) e.g. cutlery
   c) e.g. armour / bulletproof vest
3) E.g. bridge supports — need to resist squashing forces.
   E.g. surfboards — need to resist bending forces.
   E.g. drill bits — need to resist twisting forces.
4) Large items might be too expensive for anyone to buy if you make them from costly materials. / Many materials are only available in standard sizes.
5) Batch production is likely to use cheaper materials.
   If you're making a one-off product, you're more likely to use a more expensive material.
6 a) durable, strong, tough, smooth surface
   b) The material she chooses must be suitable for the manufacturing method she's planning to use.
   c) It would be expensive to use non-standard forms.

Page 41 — Metals

1) Metal ores contain the metal along with other substances.
2) The metal is separated from the other substances in the ore (often in a blast furnace). Molten metal is poured into a casting machine where it's cooled and run through rollers to make blocks.
3) Metals usually still have some impurities after they've been processed. Some products need very pure metal, so the impurities have to be removed.
4) Digging up the metal ore damages the landscape.
   The processing and refining plants produce air/water pollution.
   Transporting the metal also produces air and noise pollution.
5) It reduces the amount of metal ore that needs to be extracted from the ground. This helps to conserve metal ore, which is a finite resource. It also saves energy.
6) In annealing, the metal is cooled slowly, making it softer and less brittle. In hardening, metal is cooled quickly and becomes harder and brittler.
7) a) tempering
   b) The metal is cleaned and then gently heated. As it gets hotter, it changes gradually from a pale straw colour to blue — the colour shows how tough it's become.
8 a) To protect it from corrosion / the weather.
   b) plastic coating, polishing, lacquering
   c) plastic coating — electrical wires, polishing — chrome bodywork on cars/bikes, lacquering — jewellery

Page 43 — Metals

1) A metal that contains iron.
2) Two from, e.g: mild steel, high-carbon steel, stainless steel.
3) Two from, e.g: aluminium, brass, copper.
4) It's made from a mixture of iron and carbon.
5) e.g. brass
6) Five from, e.g: sheet, strip, bars, pipe, angle, U-shaped channel, I-shaped girder.
7) Yes — copper is a good conductor of electricity and is ductile.
8) High-carbon steel — it's hard so won't dent when it is used.
9) It doesn't rust / corrode.
10) a) Aluminium — it's lightweight and corrosion-resistant.
    b) E.g. cost, the shapes and sizes it's available in.

Page 45 — Plastics

1) When they're heated they undergo a chemical change and become hard and rigid. Once you've heated and moulded them once they can't be melted and reshaped again.
2) a) e.g. acrylic / ABS / polystyrene / polythene
   b) e.g. melamine-formaldehyde / polyester resin / epoxy resin / urea-formaldehyde
3) E.g. melamine-formaldehyde — it will not melt when the pan gets hot.
4) Five from, e.g: powder, granules, pellets, liquid, film, sheets, rods, tubes.
5) a) It's durable / resistant to corrosion.
   b) Using wet-and-dry paper.
6) Crude oil is extracted from the ground. The oil is taken to a refinery where it's processed into different substances. Some of these are then processed further to make plastics.

Answers

7) Two from, e.g: Crude oil used to make plastics is a finite resource, and we are using it up very quickly. / They take hundreds of years to degrade if they're disposed of in landfill. / Turning crude oil into plastic produces a lot of pollution/uses a lot of energy.

Page 47 — Wood and Boards

1) e.g. pine / cedar / yew
2) e.g. oak / mahogany / beech / elm
3) They are slower growing.
4) Natural timber is made when wood from trees is felled and sliced up into planks and boards. Manufactured board is made by combining different types of wood, or combining wood with other materials, e.g. chipboard is made by compressing wood particles together with glue.
5) a)

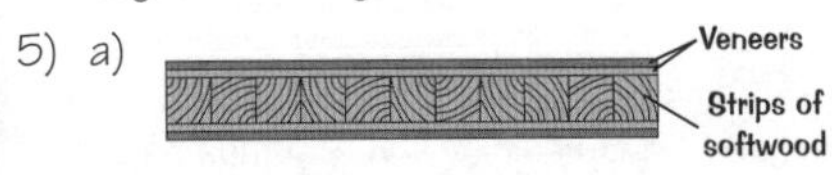

b) Two from, e.g: chipboard / MDF / plywood
c) chipboard — cheap self-assembly furniture, MDF — kitchen cabinets, plywood — building and furniture
d) They contain glue.

6) a) e.g. oak / mahogany / beech / elm
b) So that the grain will show.

7) More trees can be replanted to replace those cut down.
8) It can be shredded to make things like compost, playground flooring or chipboard. Good quality wood, e.g. undamaged floorboards, can be cleaned up and reused to make furniture.

Page 49 — Composites and New Materials

1) A composite material is made from two or more materials bonded together.
2) a) It's much stronger.
b) Two from, e.g: bullet-proof vests, racing cars, helmets
3) glass-reinforced plastic — car bodies and boats
4) a) A material that reacts to changes in the environment.
b) If it's bent, it returns to a remembered shape when it's heated.
c) e.g. to make glasses frames
d) e.g. thermochromic ink
5) A material made from very, very small particles.
6) He might have added an antibacterial coating.
7) E.g. carbon nanotubes can be added to carbon fibre to make really light bike frames.
8) Because nanoparticles are so small they could 'escape' into the environment, causing problems we don't understand yet.

Page 51 — Fixtures and Fittings

1) flush hinge
2) a) butt hinge
b) tee hinge
3) You can lift the door off the hinge.
4) E.g. steel / brass — the material needs to be strong.
5) They hold a door closed without locking.
6) a)

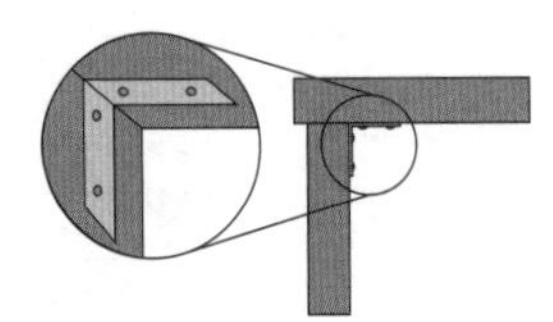

b) It's easy to take the joints apart.

Page 53 — Adhesives

1) gluing wood
2) e.g. contact adhesive
3) e.g. acrylic cement
4) a) Mix the two substances together in equal parts. When they're mixed, apply to the tiles, stick them to the wood and leave to harden for at least 15 minutes.
b) It's expensive.
5) exterior PVA
6) a) He should use it in a well-ventilated place.
b) Acrylic cement gives off harmful fumes.

Page 55 — Electrical Systems

1) input, process, output
2) a) copper wire
b) It's a good conductor of electricity.
3) batteries
4) LDR (light-dependent resistor)
5) a) Thermistors turn a circuit on or off depending on the temperature.
b) buzzer

Page 57 — Mechanical Systems

1) a) Moving backwards and forwards in a straight line.
b) Moving backwards and forwards in an arc.
c) Moving in a circle.
d) Moving in a straight line in one direction.
2)

Driver gear Driven gear

3) It makes the driver and driven gears rotate in the same direction.
4) a) rotary and linear
b) E.g. on railways where the track is steep.
5) a) bevel gear
b) e.g. a hand drill
c) A worm drive and worm wheel.

Page 59 — Mechanical Systems

1) a) a belt drive
b) Movement can be transferred from one rotating shaft to another.
2) a) On a bike.
b) The size of the sprockets.
3) a) a single pulley / a block and tackle
b) Single pulley — changes the direction of the force required, so she can lift the load by pulling downwards. / Block and tackle — she only needs to use half the force she'd need otherwise.
4) a) Cams change rotary motion into reciprocating motion.
b) To reduce friction.
c) pear cam
d) e.g. snail cam four-lobed cam

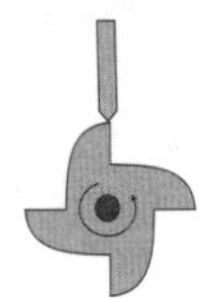

Answers

Page 61 — Mechanical Systems

1) E.g. wind-up radio, a go-kart with pedals

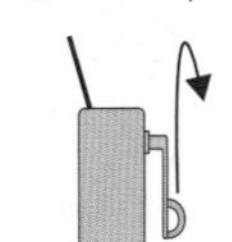

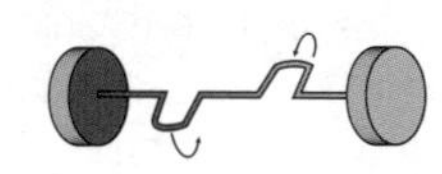

2)

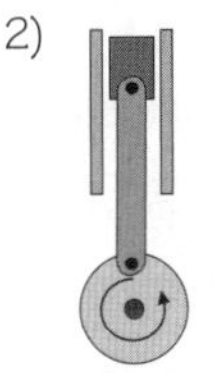

3)

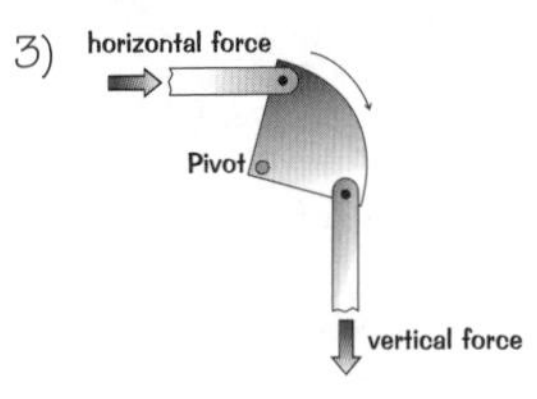

4) a) First class levers have the pivot in the middle.
Second class levers have the load in the middle.

b)

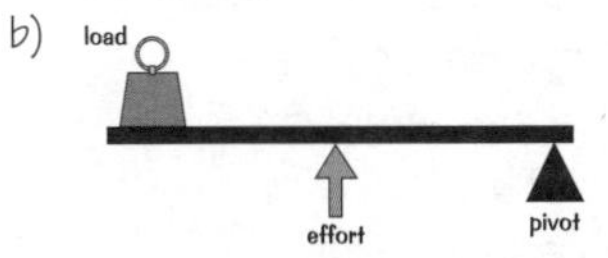

5) a) Move the pivot closer to the load.
b) first class

Page 63 — Social and Environmental issues

1) E.g. Consumers could be offended by the product. Workers could be harmed by poor working conditions / accidents.

2) Choice of material, manufacture, using the product, product disposal.

3) Repair, Reuse, Recycle, Rethink, Reduce, Refuse

4) E.g. recycle — he could use a plastic that is recyclable,
refuse — he could keep packaging to a minimum,
rethink — he could design a 'two in one' knife and spoon,
etc.

5) E.g. Use a minimum amount of material. Use recycled cardboard. Design the boxes so they can be transported flat and then folded — this will save fuel for transport. Label them clearly so that they can be recycled.

Page 65 — Health and Safety

1) a) face mask/goggles, gloves, (breathing apparatus)
b) gloves, apron and face shield
c) goggles, face mask, gloves
d) all-body suit, face shield, gauntlets, spats

2) Any four from: Never leave any machines unattended while switched on. / Know how to switch off and isolate machines in an emergency. / Ensure that any dust extraction equipment is working properly. / Never adjust a machine until you've switched it off and isolated it from the mains first. / Make sure nobody will distract you or knock you when you're working on the machine.

3) Control of Substances Hazardous to Health. They protect people from the effects of hazardous materials and processes.

4) cuttings fly off — wear goggles,
clothing catches — wear apron/roll up sleeves,
hair gets trapped — tie long hair back,
someone knocks you — make sure you're the only person working at machine,
work falls off — secure work safely,
dust inhalation — wear a face mask/provide adequate ventilation/ dust extraction,
sparks — wear goggles and gloves and keep flammable substances away from work area.

Page 67 — Scale of Production

1) jobbing / one-off, batch, mass, continuous

2) A lot of skilled labour and time is needed to make a one-off product.

3) a) batch production
b) So they can switch between making batches of different things.

4) The time needed to set up machinery, etc. for batches of a different product. It reduces efficiency because nothing is being made to sell during that time.

5) a) mass production
b) Most of the staff don't need to be highly skilled.

6) Fred only works on the spray painting stage. The other stages in the process are done by other workers.

7) a) It runs all the time, with machines designed specifically for the job.
b) Most products aren't needed in such vast quantities.

Page 69 — Manufacturing in Quantity

1) Marking out the same shape many times, and checking the accuracy of cutting.

2) a) One of, e.g: drilling — a jig is used to guide the drill, making dovetail joints — a jig is used to guide the cutting tools.
b) You don't need to spend time doing complex measuring and marking out.

3) Moulds are expensive so you need to wait until you've finalised your designs and to see if you will have large enough sales for industrial moulds to be cost-effective.

4) a) Technology/Machinery — to make products more quickly and efficiently.
Stock/premises — room and capacity to make more stuff.
Staff/Employees — to operate and maintain the machines.
Organisation/Managers — to plan and run everything smoothly.
Transport/vehicles — to get products to the customers.
b) Each product will be cheaper to make because of savings on wages, energy and wasted materials. Materials will be cheaper to buy because suppliers will give bulk discounts
c) That you may not sell enough products to pay back the loan.

Index

Index

Index